GiveWin

An Interface to Empirical Modelling

GiveWin
An Interface to Empirical Modelling

Jurgen A. Doornik
David F. Hendry

INTERNATIONAL THOMSON BUSINESS PRESS
I (T) P An International Thomson Publishing Company

London • Bonn • Boston • Johannesburg • Madrid • Melbourne • Mexico City • New York • Paris
Singapore • Tokyo • Toronto • Albany, NY • Belmont, CA • Cincinnati, OH • Detroit, MI

GiveWin: An Interface to Empirical Modelling

British Library Cataloguing-in-Publication Data
A catalogue record for this book is available from the British Library

Library of Congress Cataloging-in-Publication Data
A catalog record for this book is available from the Library of Congress

---

First edition 1996

Printed in the UK by Clays Ltd, St Ives plc

ISBN 1-86152-055-7

International Thomson Business Press   International Thomson Business Press
Berkshire House   20 Park Plaza
High Holborn   14th Floor
London WClV 7AA   Boston MA 02116
UK   USA

http://www.itbp.com

Contents

Figures

Tables

Preface

GiveWin achieves a long-standing ambition: to have a complete separation of the front-end (for data manipulation and visualization) and the econometric and statistical modules. Advances in operating system technology have made it possible to have this separation, while maintaining a reliable communication channel between the modules and GiveWin. The benefits of this are that both components can be developed separately, and changes in GiveWin would not affect the modules. C++ classes for interfacing with GiveWin will be made available.

GiveWin is written in a mixture of C and C++. The interface of GiveWin relies heavily on the Microsoft Foundation Class. GiveWin has a completely new graphics system (vector graphics at last), which was initially developed for Ox.

Ox, an object-oriented matrix programming language, is one of the modules which can interface with GiveWin. Ox is bundled with GiveWin, and we expect that some future modules will do their computations in Ox, rather than in lower level C or C++.

Although GiveWin is a new program, it builds on earlier versions of PcGive, and we wish to reiterate our thanks from the PcGive preface to all those who have helped in its development. In relation to this new version of GiveWin, we wish to thank Gunnar Bårdsen, Mike Clements, Neil Ericsson and Neil Shephard for their helpful comments. We also wish to thank International Thomson Business Press, and especially Steven Reed.

We wish you enjoyable and productive use of
GiveWin for Windows

Part I

GiveWin Prologue

Chapter 1

Introduction

GiveWin[1] is an interactive menu-driven graphics-oriented program, which acts as the 'front-end' to a series of integrated software modules. These modules obtain their data from GiveWin and return output and graphics to it. GiveWin is the component that allows you to load, edit, and save data; transform that data using the GiveWin calculator or algebra; create a wide variety of graphs, which can be edited, amended and saved in various formats; provide the data for other modules to analyse; receive their text output, results, and graphics; and lets you edit, amend, and save any or all of these as desired. As such, GiveWin can be seen as an operating system for econometric and statistical modelling.

This introductory chapter explains the conventions of the documentation, describes the Help system, sketches GiveWin's interactive operation, program control and its menu structure, then notes the data storage format and how results (both text and graphics) are saved, including a brief explanation of the various filenames and extensions used. Finally it notes the GiveWin languages (algebra and batch).

1.1 Documentation conventions

The convention for instructions that you should type is that they are shown in Typewriter font. Capitals and lower case are only distinguished as the names of variables in the program and the mathematical formulae you type. Once GiveWin has started, then from the keyboard, the Alt key accesses line menus (at the top of the screen); from a mouse, click on the item to be selected using the left button. Common commands have a shortcut on the toolbar, the purpose of which can be ascertained by placing the mouse on the relevant icon. Icons that can currently operate are highlighted. Commands on menus, toolbar buttons, and dialog items (buttons, checkboxes etc.) are shown in Sans Serif font.

---

[1]GiveWin is written in C and C++, and operates under Windows, preferably 95 or NT, but feasibly under 3.1, once version 1.30 of Win32S has been installed.

We assume that you have the basic skills to operate programs under the Windows operating system. Generally, we assume a mouse is used for operations: substitute Alt+key otherwise. We will describe operations under Windows 95: there may be some small differences under (say), Windows 3.1.

Equations are numbered as (chapter.number); for example, (8.1) refers to equation 8.1, which is the first equation in Chapter 8. References to sections have the form §chapter.section, for example, §8.1 is Section 8.1 in Chapter 8. Tables and Figures are shown as Figure chapter.number (e.g.) Figure 5.2 for the second figure in Chapter 5. Multiple graphs are numbered from left to right and top to bottom, so b is the top-right graph of four, and c the bottom left.

1.2 Help

GiveWin incorporates an extensive, context-sensitive, cross-referenced help system which offers advice about crucial decisions and can be accessed at any time. Context-dependent help can be obtained either by pressing the F1 key or clicking the context-help icon (shown as ↖?). General help is shown by either Alt+h or clicking on the Help menu (? tells you about GiveWin and the resources available on your computer). There are help topics, where you type the letters of any aspect about which help is desired; and contents where you click on items of interest. If in doubt when using GiveWin, press F1 or Alt+h to get help: this facilitates its use as you are less likely to get stuck. The cross-referencing within help is shown by the highlighted keywords: click on these (or use the Tab key to mark and press ↩) to jump to the relevant help item. The buttons at the top of each help screen allow you to retrace your steps or move sequentially between items. The Esc key clears help.

Many help, advisory, and warning messages are interspersed throughout the program to pop up as needed. Most of these are self-explanatory queries or comments.

1.3 Modular structure

The introduction to this chapter already discussed the modular structure of this new generation of econometric and statistical software.

Two such modules, for single equation econometric modelling (PcGive) and system modelling (PcFiml) in combination with Givewin, are generically called **PcGive Professional**. At the moment of writing, PcFiml is still under development. Other modules currently being developed are: STAMP (structural time series analyser, modeller and predictor) and PcNaive (for interactive Monte Carlo experimentation).

Supplied with GiveWin is a powerful object-oriented matrix programming language called **Ox**. Ox allows you to write your own programs using high level matrix operations, and provides easy facilities to read the same data files as GiveWin can load.

When the preprogrammed options in other GiveWin modules do not provide a required estimator or test, and you have some basic programming skills, Ox could be used instead. Ox also has preprogrammed classes (a class is a term in object-oriented programming) to facilitate writing Monte Carlo experiments. Ox tends to be faster than other popular matrix languages. Please consult the separate Ox documentation for further information. The **OxRun** dialog application allows running Ox programs with GiveWin as the destination of text and graphical output. An interesting example which shows densities and QQ plots while a Monte Carlo experiment is in progress is provided in \ox\samples\simula\simnor.ox.

Modules communicate with GiveWin through a process called OLE automation. This allows the modules to be completely separate (in their own address space), while communicating with GiveWin. Using the appropriate tools (and C/C++ programming skills) you can write your own modules for GiveWin. All communication is done through a basic set of around 25 function calls. Shortly after release we shall document these calls. Please contact the authors if you wish to develop additional modules for GiveWin, or check the WWW page as referred to at the end of this chapter.

1.4 Interactive operation

The GiveWin program is interactive and menu-driven. That is, at each stage a set of options is available, any one of which may be selected. Choices are made by holding down the Alt key (as noted, instructions to be typed by the user are shown in Typewriter fonts), and typing a single letter corresponding to the underlined letter on-screen of the menu or dialog to be accessed. Alternatively, use the arrow keys to place the cursor on the desired option, and then press the Enter key (shown as ↩ hereafter) to implement. A third alternative is to place the mouse cursor on the menu option and click with the left button. At any point, it is possible to access all menus that make sense: unavailable options are shown in an unlighted form.

Whenever a dialog is accessed, a default has been set such that pressing only the ↩ key (Enter key) or clicking OK suffices to accept the default.

1.5 The basics of using the program

Program control operates through holding down the Alt key while typing a letter, or using a mouse to click on a keyword, in order to select from a menu or make choices in a dialog.

Menus offer a list of mutually-exclusive alternatives of which any one can be selected, whereas the dialogs describe the available settings. For example, the Tools menu allows choices between Graphics, its setup, the calculator, algebra, etc. Only one of these is possible at any time. The Graphics dialog, by way of contrast, presents the complete set of graphing options, letting you select a wide range of alternatives, perhaps differently for every variable. The relevant menu of main operations is always visible and accessible at the top of the screen; from there, other menus and dialogs can be pulled down.

Other important keys are the Tab key (shown as $\stackrel{|\leftarrow}{\rightarrow|}$) which moves the cursor between options within a dialog; the enter key $\leftrightarrow$ which implements a choice; the arrow ($\leftarrow\uparrow\downarrow\rightarrow$) and paging keys (PgUp, PgDn, Home and End) which move around windows; the Esc key which cancels instructions or escapes from dialogs; F1 which provides context-sensitive help; the Ctrl and Shift ($\Uparrow$) keys which alter the operation of other keys; and the Del and Ins keys for editing.

Program control is most easily implemented by using a mouse: operations can be conducted by clicking the left mouse button to select, clicking twice to implement, and clicking and holding down the left button while moving the mouse to drag the cursor (for example, to mark a block of text for cutting and pasting). Any combination of mouse and keyboard is feasible when either would do the job alone. Chapter 2 discusses important key combinations when marking lists of variables for selection. Under Windows 95 and Windows NT, clicking the right mouse button will bring up a context-sensitive menu.

Windows can be moved and resized as desired (activate the system menu by clicking on the open-window icon ($-$ in Windows 3.1) in the top-left corner, or use the mouse to 'pick up' one of the borders). Multiple windows may be opened simultaneously, with cutting and pasting between edit fields.

For data samples, reference is by the absolute date in the form **Year Period** to **Year Period** (for example, 1965 1 to 1985 3). Whenever a sample choice has to be made, GiveWin will show the maximum available and will not allow choices outside that range.

1.6 Menu structure

The menu structure is shown at the top of the screen, but the facilities provided by any menu once it 'drops down' depend on whether the focus is text, graphics or data.

(1) File: data input, output, and file handling;
(2) Edit: editing window information (text, graphics, data);
(3) View: setting fonts (text, data); keeping graphs, reading from graphs (graphics);
(4) Tools: data transformation and graphing, batch files and setups;
(5) Window: selecting the window focus;
(6) Help: access to the contents and index of the help system.

Once data are loaded in GiveWin, any order or choice of menus is possible. The use of the various menus is explained in the tutorials, and more detailed descriptions can be found in the technical manuals in Part III.

1.7 Data storage

The primary mode of data storage is a pair of files with extensions **.IN7** and **.BN7**. The latter is a binary file containing the actual data, whereas the former holds the information on the contents of the binary file such as variable names, sample periods, frequencies etc. The information file is a human-readable file, the .BN7 is binary and is not human-readable. One artificial data set is supplied in the GiveWin directory, in the files called DATA.IN7 and DATA.BN7. The tutorials use this data set. If you want to load your own data, you must begin by inputting the observations; however, follow the relevant tutorial first.

GiveWin checks for potential overwriting of files and if such is likely to occur, allows selecting another file name. For text files, an additional option is to append to an existing file. The data options facilitate easy archiving of data. Please be careful not to overwrite precious data sets. It is always wise to make regular backups of important files: hard disks may break down, accidental deletion occur or viruses could strike.

GiveWin can read and write human-readable (ASCII) files and the following spread-sheet files (see Chapter 8 for detailed information):

- Excel: .XLS files (up to version 4);
- Lotus: .WKS, .WK1 files.

Gauss data files can be read but not written.

1.8 Results storage

All text results are shown in the Results window as calculations proceed but are not stored on disk or diskette unless specifically requested. On long runs, a large amount of information can be generated. This can be edited to eliminate redundant records: the Edit menu allows copying, cutting and pasting, deleting, finding and replacing. At intervals, however, the edit window may become full, forcing you to save the contents to disk, and enabling GiveWin to discard the contents from RAM (making space for new results). This happens rarely, because each Results window can hold upto 16 megabytes of text.

The storage facility allows rapid interactive modelling to proceed while any useful results can be printed as a batch job when the computer is otherwise idle. Results files can be on a different drive or directory from GiveWin.

Since much of the output is graphical, disk space should be allowed for saving graphs. Graphs can be Kept via the View menu during a run, or saved in a variety of formats as noted in the next section.

1.9 Filenames and their extensions

All file names have automatic default extensions which need not be input: a detailed discussion is provided in Chapter 8. Say the basic data set is called M1UKQ, then the information file might be M1UKQ.IN7, the associated binary file (of actual data) will be M1UKQ.BN7, the GiveWin Results window storage file could be M1UKQ.OUT (an ASCII format), the algebra storage file M1UKQ.ALG, and batch files M1UKQ.FL. A human-readable base data file generally uses the .DAT extension. Graph files allow saving in encapsulated postscript (.EPS), Windows metafiles (.WMF), enhanced metafiles (.EMF), and GiveWin graphics (.GWG), of which the last can be re-read by GiveWin for further editing.

GiveWin reports information about files and directories on-screen whenever such is wanted. On input, pre-existence is essential and a search procedure across directories and drives is easily implemented within the Open File dialog if the desired file is not found initially. On output, GiveWin will issue a warning when trying to overwrite an existing file, offering the choice between overwriting the file, or selecting a new destination file name (or appending for text files).

1.10 GiveWin languages

GiveWin is a menu-driven program for ease of use, but some operations can be implemented by entering commands. These commands are parts of simple 'computer languages' which allow Algebra and Batch operations.

1.10.1 Algebra

The Algebra command enables you to transform the database variables by typing mathematical formulae into an editor. Such algebra code can be saved, reloaded, and edited. For example, the Calculator writes its operations as algebra code to the Results window, from where it can be cut and pasted into the algebra editor.

Algebra is a simple vector language, operating on the variables in the database. This object is manipulated as a whole, although it is possible to limit access to a subsample.

1.10.2 GiveWin batch language

GiveWin allows you to load data, append results, implement algebra and save current PcGive (or PcFiml, STAMP etc.) models in batch files. Later, these can be run from the Tools menu or by clicking on the 'moving paper' icon (the paper sheet with the three horizontal red arrows pointing right). Thus, when a complicated model has been created interactively, it can be saved as a batch file for further editing, or easy recall in a later session. This is also the most convenient way to create a batch file.

Once saved to disk, a batch file can also be run directly using File/Open, or even by double clicking on the batch file in the Explorer or File Manager. Batch files have the .FL extension, which originally stood for Fiml Language.

1.11 Registry

Conforming to new practice, GiveWin and its client modules store their setup and persistent data in the registry, not in an .ini file.

1.12 Citation

To facilitate replication and validation of empirical findings, the module used to generate the results should be cited in all reports and publications involving its application.

1.13 World Wide Web

Consult http://www.nuff.ox.ac.uk/Users/Doornik/ for pointers to additional information relevant to the current and future versions of GiveWin.

Chapter 2

Getting Started

This second chapter discusses some of the basic skills required to get started with GiveWin. Since GiveWin provides the data which other modules analyse, and receives all the text output and graphics which you create in (say) PcGive, you should begin by briefly learning how GiveWin works.

When you start a module, for example, PcGive, it automatically starts up GiveWin (or will connect to the version which is already active). Then GiveWin will ask PcGive if it can handle batch commands (which it can, but other modules might not). Note that GiveWin will *not* automatically start PcGive. Once GiveWin has started, you will be able to load data, create graphs, and transform data using the GiveWin calculator or algebra. When you exit GiveWin but leave PcGive open, PcGive will have become an orphan. It will be necessary to close PcGive, and restart it to reconnect to GiveWin.

In the coming tutorials, we shall be using GiveWin as a stand-alone program. There are quite a few interesting things to be done even without using additional modules!

2.1 Starting GiveWin

Start GiveWin from the taskbar (or from the GiveWin group). If this is the first time you have used GiveWin, you might wish to reset the size of the various windows. Catch the edge of the relevant window with the mouse pointer which should change form to a double arrow, and expand or contract as desired. Your initial screen could look like the capture shown on the next page.

Clicking on a menu item (e.g., File, Edit etc.) drops down the menu as shown on page 12 for File. Then moving the arrow keys drops down each menu in turn. For example, clicking on Window shows the open windows, and clicking on the desired choice makes it the focus; if part of that window shows on screen, directly clicking on it with the mouse also works.

10

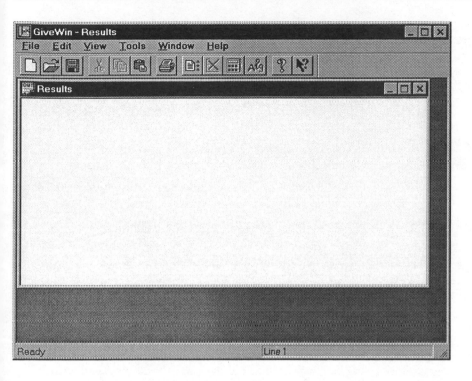

2.2 Loading and viewing the tutorial data set

Without data, there is not much that can be done, so the first step is to load data. All the tutorials use a data set called DATA.IN7. These are artificial data on consumption, income, inflation and output, denoted by CONS, INC, INFLAT, and OUTPUT respectively. The IN7 extension indicates a GiveWin data file (a format which has remained the same for versions 7 and 8 of PcGive and now for GiveWin). The IN7 file is a human-readable file, describing the data (variable names, frequency, sample period, document-ation etc.). There is a companion BN7 file, which holds the actual numbers (in binary format, so this file cannot be edited). GiveWin can handle a wide range of data files, among them Excel (.XLS up to version 4) and Lotus files (.WKS and .WK1), and of course plain human-readable (ASCII) files. You can also cut and paste data series directly from spreadsheet (but not formulae).

We shall load the tutorial data set here. Access the File menu in GiveWin:

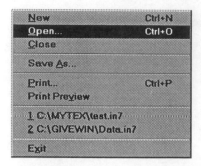

and choose Open. If you installed in the default directory structure, the data will be in the directory \GiveWin, so locate that directory and select Data:

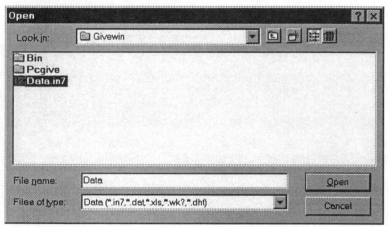

Tip By default, Windows 95 does *not* show extensions of registered file types. These include the .IN7 file type. If you wish to see the .IN7 (or any other registered) extension, start the Windows Explorer. Access View/Options, and deselect the option labelled: Hide MS-DOS file extensions for files that are registered.
It is also possible to do this for .IN7 files only: again in View/Options in the Explorer, access the File Types page. Locate GiveWin in the list of registered file types, select it, and push the Edit button. Then mark Always show extension.

The data file will be loaded, and displayed minimized:

If the filename is not present, to change directory click the down triangle to the right of 'Look in' and move to the relevant directory. Once the data are loaded, click on the 'overlapping boxes' icon to restore the window to full size and show the contents of the database:

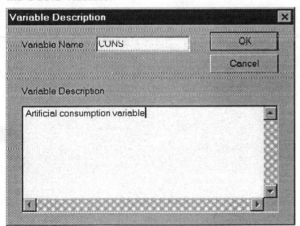

Data				
	CONS	INC	INFLAT	OUTPUT
1953- 1	890.45	908.212	3.6595	1203.77
1953- 2	886.543	900.679	2.7649	1200.36
1953- 3	886.329	899.795	2.521	1193.63
1953- 4	884.885	898.482	1.717	1193.04
1954- 1	885.254	895.777	.9729	1194.11
1954- 2	884.528	894.831	.676	1191.03
1954- 3	884.436	892.741	.1739	1191.47
1954- 4	884.311	892.768	-.3302	1195.34
1955- 1	887.426	896.971	-.4645	1195.51
1955- 2	889.556	901.406	-.3819	1198.2
1955- 3	890.659	901.479	-.2016	1199.24
1955- 4	894.079	905.117	.1956	1203.88

Although data values are stored internally with about 15 to 16 digit accuracy (8 byte reals), the data are displayed with 6 digits only in the spreadsheet. On the bottom right of the GiveWin window, in the status bar, the observation under the cursor is shown with full accuracy.

Double clicking on the variable name shows the documentation of the variable. For the CONS variable:

Variable Description

Variable Name `CONS`

OK

Cancel

Variable Description

`Artificial consumption variable`

The data can be manipulated, much like in a spreadsheet program. Double clicking on an observation brings up a revision box, where corrected values can be entered (or missing values set to an observed outcome). Single clicking, and maintaining the button depressed, then dragging the mouse highlights a block of data which can be copied to the clipboard for insertion in another part of the database (click on the two pages icon for copy, or the `Ctrl+Ins` key; paste is the clipboard icon or the `Shift+Ins` key). To *minimize* the window again, click on the '–' icon. Clicking on the 'x' *closes* the window and so removes the database from GiveWin (unlike in PcGive version 8). If the data have been altered, GiveWin will enquire about saving the revised database before exiting it. More generally, any window's contents can be saved as a file by clicking on the File menu and selecting Save As for new files (or the third icon on the toolbar, looking like a diskette).

2.3 GiveWin graphics

The graphics facilities of GiveWin are powerful yet easy to use. This section will show you how to make time plots and cross plots of variables in the database. GiveWin offers automatic selections of scaling etc., but you will be able to edit these graphs, and change the default layout such as line colours and line types. Graphs can also be saved in a variety of formats for later use in a word processor, or for reloading into GiveWin.

2.3.1 A first graph

Graphics is the first entry on the Tools menu. Activate that command to see the following dialog box (or click on the cross-plot icon on the toolbar):

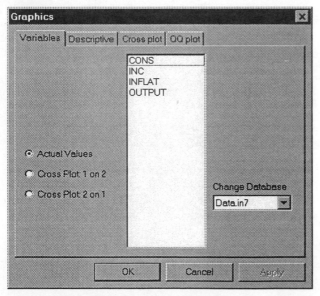

This is the first example of a dialog with a multiple selection list box. In such a list box you mark as many items as you want. Here we mark all the variables we wish to graph. With the keyboard you can only mark a single variable (by using the arrow up and down keys), or range of variables (hold the shift key down while using the arrow up or down keys).

With the mouse there is more flexibility:

- single click to select one variable;
- hold the left mouse button down to select a range of variables;
- hold the Ctrl key down and click to select additional variables;
- hold the Shift key down and click to extend the selection range.

In this example we select CONS and INC and then press the OK button. Now the graph appears, which looks very much like Figure 2.1. The only difference is the position of the legend. You can pick that up with the mouse, and move it to another position in the graph as desired.

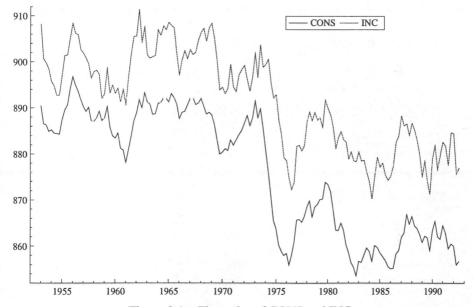

Figure 2.1   Time plot of CONS and INC.

Most graphs in this book are boxed in, obtainable by choosing Graphics Setup from the Tools menu, and selecting the Layout page then clicking on Boxed. The View and Edit menu show the available options for graphs.

Let's try the pointing option. Select Point from the View menu (the menus change according to whether focus is in a text, graphics or data window; here we assume you kept the graph active), and move the mouse. You see that the status bar at the foot of the GiveWin window displays the graph coordinates, for example:

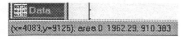

The first coordinates are the pixel coordinates (not screen pixels, but 'paper' pixels), followed by the area (here only one: area 0), and the real world coordinates which deliver the actual values of the variables at the mouse point (only areas have real world coordinates, also see Chapter 10).

2.3.2 Multiple graphs

One of the powerful features of GiveWin is the ability to draw multiple graphs simultaneously on-screen. We shall now get two graphs on screen. Click on the Graphics toolbar button, select both CONS and INC again, click on Cross plot 1 on 2. A new feature of GiveWin is that graphs can now be edited and features added while they are on screen, and after adding other graphs if desired. Double click on the cross plot graph, select Regression, Scale in the Graphics Properties dialog, and add one regression line as shown:

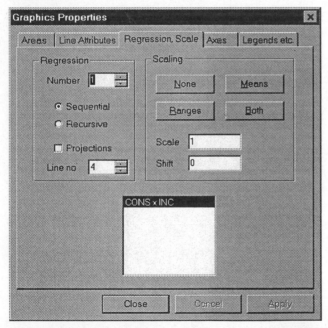

The result is shown in Figure 2.2.

 The editing possibilities are manifold: Chapter 3 provides a detailed discussion, but you can always play around with graphs at your leisure.

2.3.3 Graph saving and printing

To print a graph directly to the printer when the graphics window has the focus, click on the printer icon in the toolbar. You can preview the result first using the Print Preview command from the File menu.

Graphs can be saved to disk in various formats:

- Windows metafile (.WMF);
- Enhanced metafile (.EMF, Windows 95 and Windows NT only);
- Encapsulated PostScript (.EPS), which is the format used to produce all the graphs in this book;
- GiveWin Graphics File (.GWG).

The GWG format is particular to GiveWin; no other program can read it and no printer can handle it. However, it is the only format which you can reload into GiveWin for further editing, at which stage the graph can be printed or saved in another format if required.

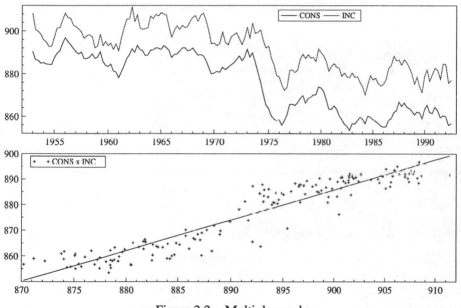

Figure 2.2   Multiple graphs.

2.3.4 Using the clipboard for graph pasting

Graphs can also be copied to the clipboard (two pages icon), then when you switch directly to another Windows application, pasted into it (e.g., a word processor or spreadsheet program). This procedure ensures that the graph is entered quickly, and can be viewed, size-adjusted etc., but it may be of a slightly different quality from that of a saved file.

Click on an area to select an individual plot within multiple graphics. When an area is selected it can also be copied to the clipboard, but not pasted to other programs (only the whole graphics window can be pasted into other programs, such as Microsoft Word).

Internally, however, individual areas can be copied and pasted. Pasting adds to an area, if an area is selected, or just increases the number of plots otherwise.

2.4 Calculator

Two options are available for transforming data: by algebra or by a dialog approach, which mimics the operation of a pocket calculator. We begin with the latter, as it is the simplest. Press on the Calculator button leading to the capture shown below (or via the Data menu and calculator choice).

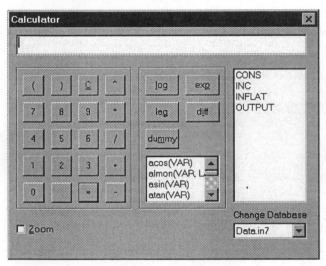

Please note that GiveWin and client modules are sensitive to the case of the variable names so that 'cons', 'Cons', and 'CONS' are treated as different variables. This can be useful for distinguishing real (lower case) from nominal (capitals) variables, or logs from levels, etc. Finally, GiveWin will offer a default name for a newly created variable in several cases:

- prefixes of 'D' for differences, e.g. DCONS;
- prefixes of 'L' for logarithms, e.g. LCONS;
- suffix '$\_n$' for n-period lags, e.g. CONS_1.

So can you guess what DLCONS_1 is likely to be?

The aim is to build up an algebraic expression (which is valid Algebra code: see §2.5). The first transformation is to take the first difference of CONS. Click on the CONS variable just to highlight it (don't double click), and then on the diff button, accept a lag length of one, to see in the top part of the dialog:

Click on the button with the = sign, and accept the default name of DCONS, which will be created in the database, and added to the list of variables. A two-period difference is just as easy to compute: select CONS, press the diff button and change the length of the differencing period.

Another transformation to try: INC–CONS. Double click on INC, click on the minus button, and then double click on CONS. The expression now reads INC–CONS, press on = to evaluate. Name the variable SAVING (you could use a name like INC–CONS, but must enclose such a name in double quotes).

Finally, we create a step dummy (or indicator variable), where the step lasts from 1979(2) to 1980(4). We need zeros outside that period, ones inside. Click on the dummy button, and enter:

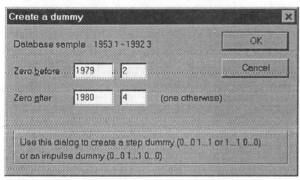

Click on OK, and then on = to create the dummy. Give it an informative name, such as s792t804.

Tip We deliberately gave no examples involving lags. For estimation in modules such as PcGive or PcFiml, lags are best created at the model formulation stage, where the programs will keep track of their presence for dynamic analyses.

Three additional operations can be performed on variables inside the listbox:

- Delete a variable: select and press the Delete key; you will have to confirm the deletion as the variable is eliminated from the database.
- Move variables: pick the variable up with the mouse, and move it to another position. This changes the order in the database.
- Rename a variable: select and press the Insert key; you will be prompted for a new name.

Exit the calculator (Esc or click on the x button), and graph some of the variables to check whether the transformations are correct. All transformations are logged to the Results window:

```
Algebra code for Data.in7:
DCONS = diff(CONS,1);
SAVING = INC-CONS;
s792t804 = dummy(1979,2, 1980,4);
```

This leads us to the next topic.

2.5 Algebra

Algebra enables us to do transformations by typing the expressions directly into an editor. It allows saving and loading from disk of a whole chunk of statements.

As an example, we rerun the transformations of the previous section. To verify if that will work, first delete the newly created variables from the database. Open the database window, click on DCONS (on the name) and press the Delete key:

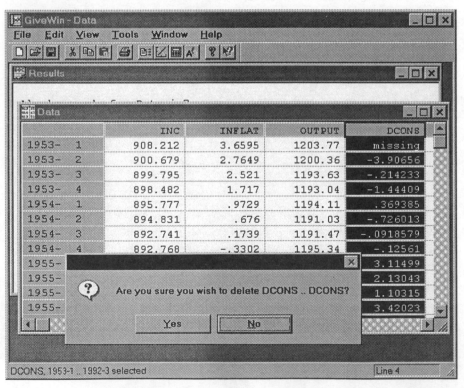

Say yes. Delete SAVING, and the dummy in the same way. Minimize the database, and set focus to the Results window. Highlight the three algebra lines, and copy them to the clipboard (Ctrl+Ins). From the Tools menu, select Algebra, and paste the code (Shift+Ins) to see the screen capture overleaf. Now press OK: run. The variables have been recreated. We can inspect the database to see what happened. The algebra code is again logged to the Results window.

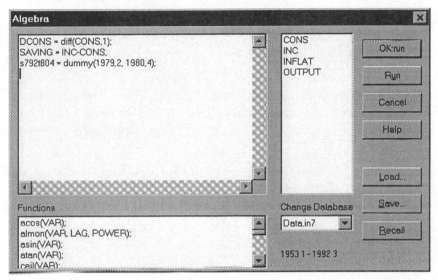

The only variable names allowed are those that would be valid names in computer languages like Ox or C: the first character must be a letter or an underscore, the rest a letter, underscore or digit. Other names must be enclosed in double quotes.

Algebra uses database variables as follows: if a left-hand variable is already in the database it will be overwritten, otherwise it will be created. Variables on the right must exist, possibly because of preceding lines of algebra code. Algebra is case-sensitive, meaning that LCONS, LCons and lcons refer to three different variables.

Tip Double-click on a function in the function list or variable in the variable list to paste it into the editor. This saves typing.

As an advanced example, we explain how it is possible to create the same dummy using the insample function and a conditional assignment. The insample function has four arguments: startyear, startperiod, endyear, endperiod. It returns 1 (or TRUE: everything which is not 0 is TRUE) if the observation under consideration falls within the sample, otherwise it returns 0 (FALSE). The conditional assignment works as follows: the conditional statement (the 'if' part) is followed by a question mark and the 'then' part, which is followed by a colon and the 'else' part. Read:

```
i1980p1 = insample(1980, 1, 1980, 1) ? 1 :  0;
```
as: i1980p1 takes on the value 1 for the observations which are in the specified sample, and the value 0 for the other observations. In this case, the same result can be obtained by writing:

```
i1980p1 = insample(1980, 1, 1980, 1);.
```

An error message pops up if you make a mistake. The error can be corrected on returning to the algebra editor.

Tip   A sensible strategy is to store algebra code and basic data only, and recompute transforms during each run: this economizes on storage and facilitates updating analyses when data are revised or corrected.

Do not save the modified data set. Either delete the newly created variables, or quit the data set, and reload the original DATA.IN7/DATA.BN7. Algebra is documented in Chapter 9. This completes the getting started chapter. The next part is taken up by tutorials on graph editing, graphics, data loading and saving, and data transformations.

Part II

GiveWin Tutorials

Chapter 3

Tutorial on Graph Editing

The prologue introduced the basics of using GiveWin, accessing its menus and dialogs, loading, saving and transforming data, using graphics, including saving, printing and pasting them, and described the Calculator and Algebra. Now we consider the flexible graphics facilities in more detail. Remember that on-line context-sensitive help is always available: click on Help or press F1. Descriptive graphics are discussed in Chapter 4. Chapter 10 discusses various graphics options more systematically.

If you're not inside GiveWin at the moment, restart and load the tutorial data set DATA.IN7/DATA.BN7.

3.1 Multiple graphs

Create DCONS and DINC as the first differences of CONS and INC, then activate the Graphics choice on tools which defaults to the Variables options as shown in Chapter 2. Mark CONS and INC, then click Apply, at which point the graph will appear, but you remain in the dialog; mark CONS and INC again, but now click on the Cross plot 1 on 2 button, then Apply; and repeat both of these operations for the pairs DCONS and DINC, clicking OK after the fourth, to see Figure 3.1. We number the four graphs from left to right and top to bottom as:

$$
\begin{array}{cc}
a & b \\
c & d
\end{array}
$$

3.2 Graphics paper

To understand the editing facilities, it is easiest to see the graphics window as a piece of graphics paper, consisting of 15 000 'pixels' along the x-axis, and 10 000 along the y-axis (this is very much higher than the actual screen resolution). The four graphs in Figure 3.1 all have an *area* attached to them. By default, these areas are evenly spread out on the paper. An area has pixel coordinates to fix it on the paper, and real world coordinates to draw variables, axes, etc. inside the area.

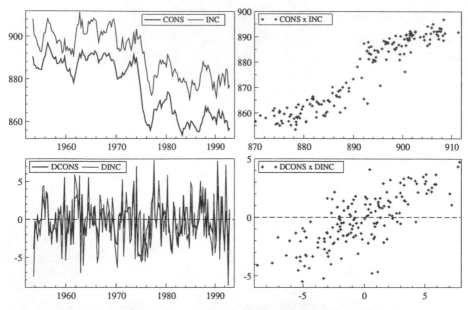

Figure 3.1   Descriptive graphics of CONS, INC, DCONS and DINC.

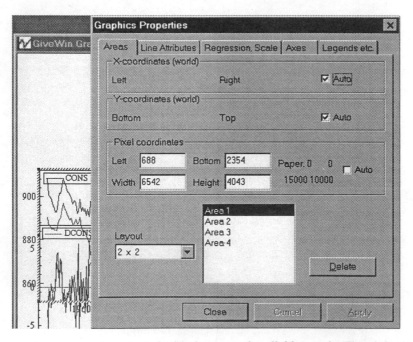

An area can be selected with the mouse by clicking on it. Then it is shown selected (in a 'fuzzy' rectangle), and you can pick it up and move it around on the paper. Once moved around, the pixel coordinates switch from Auto to manual. To see this, double click on the area (or use Edit/Edit Graph) and select the Areas page.

Click on Auto to reset to the original paper location. Similarly, it is possible to redefine the world coordinates of the area (e.g. to zoom in on a part of the graph). With four graphs on paper, various ways of layout can be chosen.

The View menu has three options relating to the paper:

- Paper Color sets a background colour for the whole piece of paper;
- Working View controls the size of the paper on screen. The default is 100, but if your computer runs in a low resolution, you could set this to 80 for example (note that the window does not automatically change size). Use Make default to keep this size between runs of GiveWin. A working view of 80 works well on a 640 × 480 screen.
- Snap to Grid activates a grid, for aligning graph objects stepwise rather than continuously.

By default, GiveWin keeps on adding graphs in the GiveWin Graphics Window. If you wish to keep the current window, and start with a clean piece of paper, use Keep Graph on the View menu. To start with a clean sheet: close the graphics window; a new one will be opened automatically when required.

3.3 Copy and paste

The use of the clipboard is discussed in §10.7.

3.4 Graphics properties

These graphs use the automatic selections by GiveWin: they are fine for immediate usage, but are open to many possible amendments depending on the purposes of the various graphs. We begin with Figure 3.1a. Double click on it to bring up the Graphics Properties dialog (a single click makes it become the focus, shown by the 'fuzzy' boxed outline mentioned before).

Here we can change the line type (e.g., to index line, as shown in Figure 3.2), or screen colours of lines for live presentations. Next, double click again on graph a, and select Regression, scale; and mark one regression line (as in §2.3.2) for CONS; highlight INC and repeat, also marking Projections.

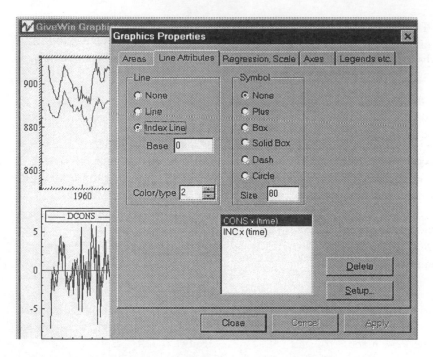

Selecting Figure 3.1b, change the symbol to a solid box, and alter its size to 90. Click on Regression, scale, and mark 4 regressions, and Projections:

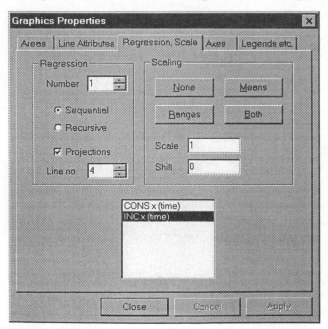

For graph c, select Axes on Graphics Properties, and click Grid, highlight Y-axis 1 and repeat, then close: on the graph, grab the legend and move it to a more convenient location (click with the mouse and holding the button, 'drag' it to the place required) as shown.

Finally for graph d, mark 20 (sequential) regression lines. This is a very different 'picture' from our first figure, and such facilities can be used to reveal hidden features of data. The final result is in Figure 3.2.

Changing Line no alters the line colour: we have done that for DCONS in c to a thicker line as explained in the next section. An individual graph in a graphics window can also be moved around or resized.

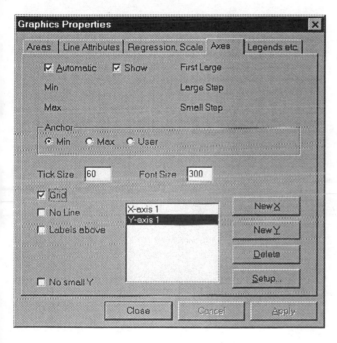

3.5 Graphics setup

There are many default settings that can be generically user controlled, and are persistent between runs of GiveWin. Click on Tools, Graphics setup to bring up the dialog shown below.

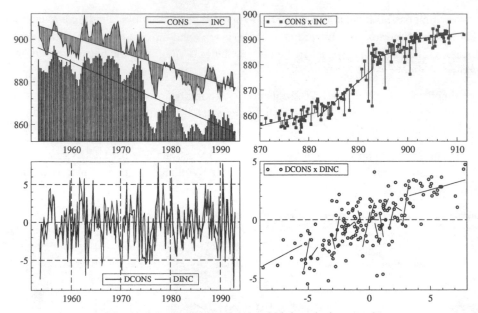

Figure 3.2   Edited and amended descriptive graph.

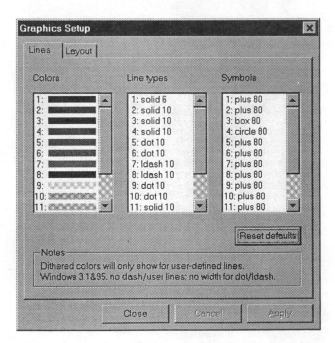

The colours, types and thickness of all lines can be set as wished: for example, much thicker lines are more useful for live demonstrations than printed graphs; some colours show much better than others, etc. Double click on a line and the dialog will offer the following possibilities (as noted in §10.6.7, not all options can be displayed on screen for some versions of Windows):

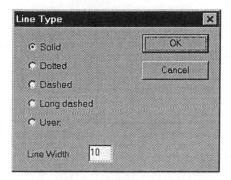

Similarly, clicking on Layout allows one to change the default settings for boxing round graphs, fonts and their sizes, axis and grid styles, tick marks, legends, whether histograms are solid (in colour) or empty etc:

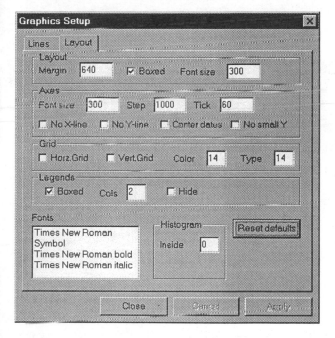

Graphics Setup can also be accessed through Setup on some pages of the Graphics Properties dialog. If only temporary changes are needed, or different settings for each graph, these can be implemented from the Graphics Properties dialog after double clicking on a graph. The operating principles are the same throughout the GiveWin system, so it is easy to develop a setup as desired – and change it quickly if needed.

3.6 Drawing

Once any graph is on screen, drawing facilities are also accessible. Close the current graphics windows, and cross plot INFLAT against OUTPUT. Double click on the graph, and set the Line Attribute to line to connect the points. Now click once on the graph so it is the focus, then click with the right mouse button (this will not work in Windows 3.1; alternatively use the Edit menu) to see:

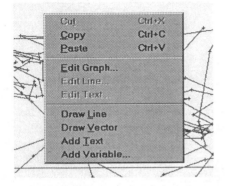

Click on Draw Line and return to the graph where the mouse point becomes like a pencil, as indeed it can now draw a line. Do so as in Figure 3.3a. Next double click on the line and a Line dialog will appear:

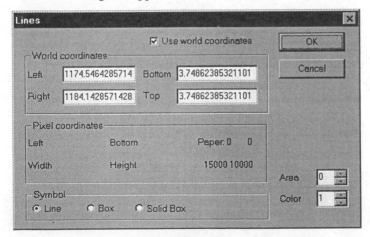

mark solid box and select colour 12. Click again on the line and grab a corner to expand it to a box as in Figure 3.3b.

Continue the expansion till the cluster of points around the low OUTPUT 'equilibrium' is highlighted as in Figure 3.3c. The box can also be picked up with the mouse and moved. If you now add another box to highlight the second equilibrium (or copy the graph on itself and then draw the boxes apart, deleting one of the unnecessary cross plots), we get the final graph in Figure 3.3d.

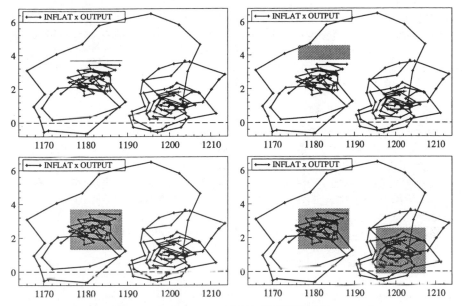

Figure 3.3   Drawing on an INFLAT/OUTPUT cross plot.

Also try the Draw Vector option. This allows for free-hand drawing (your name for example). This creates a vector, which will appear in the list of variables in the Graphics Properties dialog (now draw a regression line through your name).

3.7 Adding text and variables

To add text, proceed as in the previous section: use the edit menu or click with the right button, and select Add text. The mouse cursor becomes a letter. Now click where you wish the text to appear. A dialog pops up in which the text is entered:

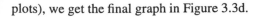

Text can be moved around using the cursor.

The last entry on the edit menu allows the addition of database variables (or cross plots), but requires selection of an area before the option becomes active. Similar results can be achieved by copying one area to the clipboard, selecting another, and pasting into that area.

3.8 Legends

Legends are automatically created for all the variables in each graph, located in the top left corner of the graph. The legend can be picked up with the mouse and moved around the graph.

Legends shrink in size as the graph gets smaller. When the graph is very small (usually with more than six graphs in one window) the legend is removed altogether (actually it is hidden).

The Legends etc. page on the Graphics Properties dialog (shown on page 38) allows 'unhiding' the legend.

Chapter 4

Tutorial on Graphics

The previous tutorial was mainly concerned with the mechanics of changing the appearance of GiveWin graphs. This chapter discusses the various types of graphs which are available for (exploratory) data analysis.

If you're not inside GiveWin at the moment, restart and load the tutorial data set DATA.IN7/DATA.BN7. Note that the foot of the File menu lists recently loaded files, and clicking on the desired choice will immediately load it. Create DCONS as the first difference of CONS.

4.1 Descriptive graphics

Activate the Graphics choice on the Tools menu, followed by the Descriptive page on the dialog. Mark Actual values, Correlogram, Spectrum, Density, Histogram and Normal as shown below.

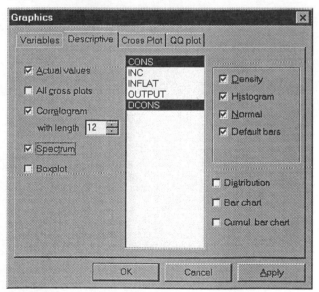

Remember: to select the two variables, click on CONS, then hold the `Ctrl` key down
and click on DCONS.

The options for each variable correspond to a time-plot showing its historical behaviour, a correlogram and spectrum which reflect its autocorrelation, and a histogram with
estimated density and the normal distribution for reference to evaluate the distributional
shape. This generates eight graphs in total, see Figure 4.1. A detailed description of the
formulae underlying these graphs is given in Chapter 7.

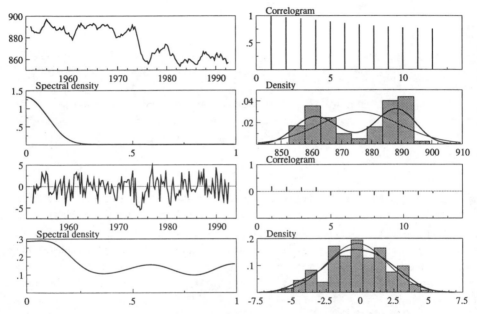

Figure 4.1   Descriptive graphics of CONS and DCONS.

4.1.1 Actual values

Shows the actual values of all selected variables, each in a separate graph. Use the Variables page to plot all selected variables inside one graph. If there are missing values,
these show up as a gap in the line.

4.1.2 All cross plots

Shows all cross plots involving the selected variables, each in a separate graph. If CONS,
INC, INFLAT and OUTPUT are marked, for example, the cross plots are: CONS on
INC, on INFLAT and on OUTPUT, INC on INFLAT and OUTPUT, and finally INFLAT
on OUTPUT. If there are missing values, these are omitted from the graphs.

4.1.3 Correlogram

The correlogram plots the correlations $\hat{r}_j^*$ between x_t and successive x_{t-j}, here for $j = 1, \ldots, 12$. Also see §7.2. The length of the correlogram can be set by the user. Since the correlation between x_t and x_t is always unity, it is not drawn in the graphs. We see that CONS remains strongly (positively) correlated with its own lags, even after 12 periods (3 years). This suggests some form of 'long memory' or non-stationarity. DCONS on the other hand shows little autocorrelation.

Tip   If you want the actual values recorded, simply regress the desired variable on a constant in PcGive and use Test, residual correlogram.

4.1.4 Spectrum

The spectrum (or more accurately here: spectral density) consists of a smoothed function of autocorrelations (that is, the correlations $\{\hat{r}_j^*\}$ in the previous section between x_t and x_{t-j}, again for $j = 1, \ldots, 12$). It is symmetric between $-\pi$ and π, and so is only graphed for $[0, \pi]$; 1 on the horizontal axis stands for π, 0.5 for 0.5π, etc. Peaks at certain frequencies can indicate regular (cyclical or seasonal) behaviour in the series. The spectrum of CONS shows the 'typical spectral shape' (a term introduced by Granger, 1966), which many macroeconomic variables appear to have: a pronounced peak at the lowest frequencies. Like the correlogram, this indicates that successive values of CONS are strongly correlated. The spectrum of DCONS is much 'flatter', indicating a series which is closer to white noise. More information is in §7.3.

4.1.5 Histogram and density

The histogram is a simple graph: the range of x_t is divided into intervals, and the number of observations in each interval is counted. The height of each bar records the number of entries in that interval. In GiveWin these are divided by the total number of observations to show the relative frequency (use bar to keep the count). GiveWin sets a default number of intervals dependent on the sample size, but this can be set by the user (click on Default bars). Using Graphics setup, the histograms can be filled in any desired colour.

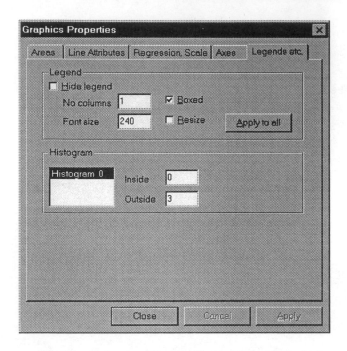

The bimodal curved line in Figure 4.1 is a smoothed version of the histogram. Because we divided the histogram by T, the height of the bars add up to one. Correspondingly, the area underneath the smoothed histogram is unity, and the curve is called a (nonparametric) density estimate. The familiar 'bell' shape of the normal distribution, is added for comparison. It is clear that CONS does not look very normal. DCONS is much closer to a normal distribution: at least it is symmetric, but could still be too narrow, or too wide (i.e., have excess kurtosis relative to the normal).

Tip If you want to test for normality, use Data/Descriptive Statistics in PcGive and select the Normality option.

If you wish the legends to appear, as shown here, double click on a graph, and uncheck both hide legend and resize. You'll probably prefer a smaller font size then.

Keep the graph, and return to click on the graphics icon, Descriptive option, this time marking Box plot, Distribution, Bar chart and cumulative Bar chart. Again we obtain eight graphs for CONS and DCONS, as shown in Figure 4.2.

4.1.6 Distribution

This shows the cumulative distribution of the variable, integrating the estimated density. The result is presented in the form of a QQ plot against the normal distribution, see §4.3.

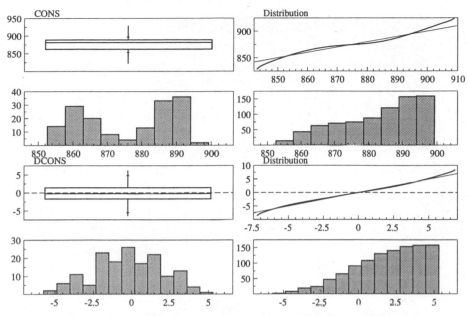

Figure 4.2   Further descriptive graphics of CONS and DCONS.

4.1.7 Bar chart

This is just an unscaled histogram, and the cumulative version literally adds up the total numbers below or inside the current interval.

4.1.8 Box plot

A box plot shows the distribution of a variable in a more condensed form. Refer to Figure 4.3, which shows the total range of a variable and the concentration in a central region, using the quartiles of the distribution, and the inter-quartile range (IQR).

4.2 Cross plotting

Click on View, Keep graph, and minimize the graph, now called Graph1, so that a new graphics window will commence in this section. Notice that this operation does not save the graph; it merely preserves the graphics window by starting a new one for the next set of graphs. Click on the graph icon and then on Cross plot. We have already seen some simple cross plots in the earlier figures, but with this option many new possibilities open up.

Click on DCONS as Y, DINC as X, and mark both Regression line and Reverse regression, so that the figure shows the lines of best fit, minimizing vertical squared deviations of points from the line for the former, and horizontal for the latter. Click OK to

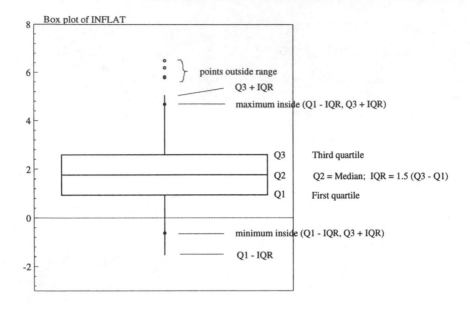

Figure 4.3   Box plot of INFLAT.

see the graph. The 'steeper' line corresponds to horizontal minimization: can you see why? To check, double click on the graph and select 1 Regression, and Projections: this will superimpose on the vertically-minimized line as shown in Figure 4.4a below.

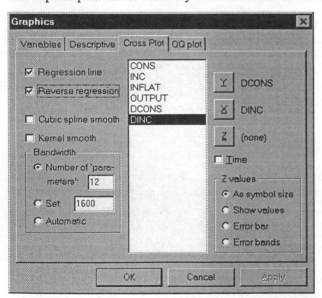

Return to the Cross plot dialog, again select DCONS as Y, DINC as X, but now mark

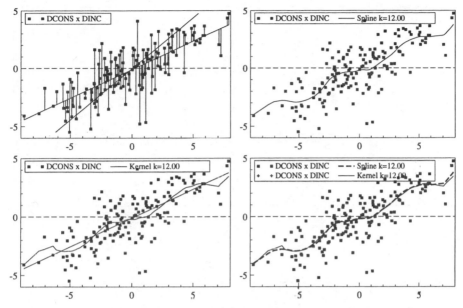

Figure 4.4   Sophisticated cross plotting graphs.

Cubic spline smooth and click OK. This is one of two ways of fitting 'smoothed' lines that nevertheless track the general movements in cross plots; the other is Kernel smooth – so draw that one next. You can fit a straight line as well for comparison (as in the Kernel graph); or be more enterprising as follows. Move the focus to the spline graph (shown by the 'fuzzy' outline) and copy it to the clipboard (two pages icon); click at the foot of the graph window, then click the clipboard icon to paste a copy of the spline graph to make a block of four. Move the focus to the kernel graph, copy it to the clipboard, focus on the *copied* spline graph, and paste the kernel on top. The direct comparison is clear: they are close approximations. And for all their 'wiggles', both are nearly straight lines. Setting the number of parameters to (say) 3 will produce a fairly smooth fit.

Next, in Algebra, set `seas=period();` then return to the Cross plot dialog, selecting DCONS as Y, DINC as X, as before, and seas as Z (highlight seas and click Z). Finally, mark Show values to produce the cross plot by seasons (4 denotes the fourth quarter). As the tutorial data are not highly seasonal, we have actually recorded the effect of this 3-way cross plot using the data on the levels and first differences of UK log consumption and disposable income from Davidson, Hendry, Srba and Yeo (1978) in Figure 4.5. In the top panel (levels), the fourth (Xmas) quarter is uniformly highest, and the first lowest; in the lower panel (first differences), the first-quarter points are grouped far below all other quarters, the second are scattered along the *x*-axis, and the last two quarters are bunched together. Thus, plotting reveals distinct patterns in this instance.

There are more cross plot options. One is a so-called bubble chart. It consists of

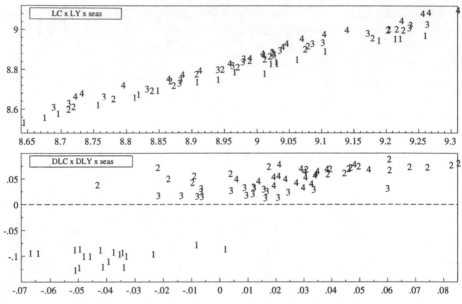

Figure 4.5   Cross plotting consumption against income by seasons.

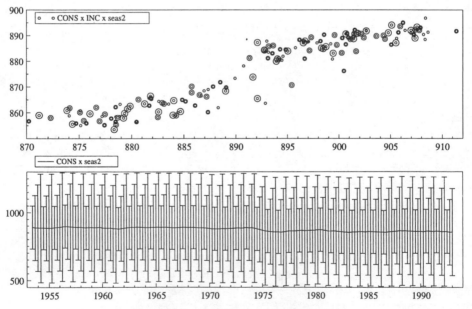

Figure 4.6   Bubble chart and error bars.

a cross plot, where the symbols are circles, and the size of the circle indicates a third dimension (e.g. market share). Create seas2 = seas*40 + 40; in Algebra, and

use the Cross Plot page to do a cross plot of CONS on INC. Then select seas2 as the
Z variable, and choose to show the Z values as Symbol size. Double click on the graph
to set the symbol to a circle. The result is in Figure 4.5. The final graph of this section
illustrates error bars/bands. Select the Cross Plot graph. Use CONS as the X variable
(click on CONS), then select Time to do a cross plot against time. Click on seas2 and Z
to make it the Z variable. As the last action choose Error bar for the type of Z variable.
See Figure 4.6.

4.3 QQ plots

The last options to be considered in this chapter concern QQ, or cross probability, plots.
As discussed in the companion book on PcGive, statisticians view variables as being
described by probability distributions. If X is the variable, and x a value it could take,
then $P_x (X > x)$ is the probability that the value is in fact greater than x. For example,
if the variable is the height of a child, when x is one metre, $P_x (X > 1)$ is the probability
that the child is taller than a metre. The values of x can be any number, but $P_x (\cdot)$ must
not be negative or exceed unity. Plotting $P_x (X > x)$ against x generates an $\int$-shaped
curve (but more stretched out horizontally), which is hard to interpret. Figure 4.7 shows
a normal and a t density together with their cumulative distributions.

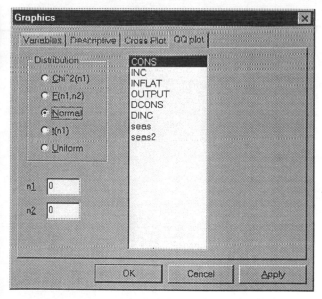

When x has a uniform distribution over $(0, 1)$, if $P_x (\cdot)$ is plotted against x in a unit
square, the result is a straight line. A similar idea applies to all distributions and QQ
plots can be selected so some reference distribution is a straight line and the empirical
distribution compared to it.

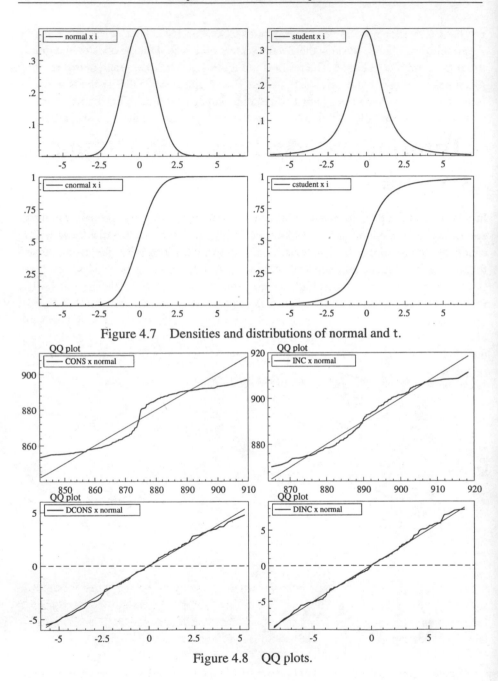

Figure 4.7   Densities and distributions of normal and t.

Figure 4.8   QQ plots.

Figure 4.8 illustrates for CONS and INC and their differences against the normal as a reference. Clearly, there is a vast range of graphics options to suit your needs.

Chapter 5

Tutorial on Data Input and Output

In this tutorial, we turn to what can be one of the more tedious operations: inputting new data. Fortunately, GiveWin can load a wide range of formats to allow for easy exchange with other programs; and can do so from disk files or by copy and paste. Table 5.1 summarizes the available options.

Table 5.1   GiveWin data input/output options.

Paper ⟶ GiveWin	Directly into database
	Using GiveWin as editor
Disk ⟶ GiveWin	Excel spreadsheets (.XLS)
	Lotus spreadsheets (.WKS,.WK1)
	ASCII (human-readable) files
	GiveWin data files (.IN7/.BN7)
	Gauss data files (.DHT/.DAT)
GiveWin ⟶ disk	Excel spreadsheets (.XLS)
	Lotus spreadsheets (.WKS,.WK1)
	ASCII (human-readable) files
	GiveWin data files (.IN7/.BN7)
GiveWin ⟶ paper	Print
GiveWin ⟶ clipboard	e.g. from GiveWin to Excel
clipboard ⟶ GiveWin	or vice versa

Many other formats can be loaded, after conversion to any of the supported formats at source. For example, to load .WK3 (a Lotus format) or .CSV (comma-separated) files: load these into Lotus or Excel, then save as .XLS or .WKS and load into GiveWin. Certain CSV files can be loaded directly as human-readable files, see Chapter 8.

The order in the tutorials below is somewhat different from the table: first we enter a small data set into GiveWin (12 observations from the tutorial data set variables CONS and INFLAT, from the first quarter of 1955 up to the last quarter of 1958). Next we save this in various formats, which we shall reload. After all, we do not want to spend too much time typing in data.

45

From now on, we will often abbreviate a menu selection; for example, File/Save as/GiveWin data (*.IN7) will mean: select the File menu, then select Save as, and then the file type GiveWin data (*.IN7).

5.1 From paper to GiveWin

GiveWin allows you to type data directly into a database, or to enter the data into a file, and then load the file.

5.1.1 Directly into the database

Start GiveWin without loading any database yet. One of the available options on the File menu is New: click on it then select Database:

In the current situation, this brings up the Create a new database dialog to ask you for the information needed to create the database. Fill in the information as shown in the screen capture: Quarterly frequency (Alt+q: or click on Quarterly), sample period 1955–1 to 1958–4 (Alt+s, 1955, Tab, 1, Tab, 1958, Tab, 4).

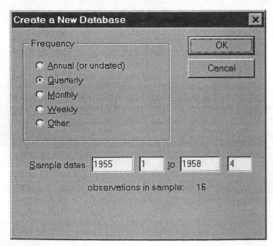

Tip The following can be noticed when typing text into an edit field: if it is in reverse colour, then typing any letter will first remove all the existing text. If you wish to modify the initial text, start by pressing Arrow left, Arrow right, Home or End, or just click in the edit field with the mouse.

Press OK to accept the dialog: the empty database appears on screen. It could be convenient here to maximize the database window: from the keyboard type Alt+spacebar, x; using the mouse, click on the □ at the top right of the database window frame (△ in Windows 3.1).

To add variables to the database, keep the focus on it and click on Edit, New variable and type Cons; repeat to create Inflat so there are two variables in the database. Alternatively, double click on the empty grey box at the column head, then enter the name of the variable to be created in the Variable description dialog:

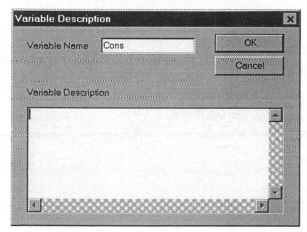

All the observations of Cons and Inflat are set to missing . This is the value GiveWin uses to indicate that the observation is missing (−9999.99 is the actual number used for the missing value). GiveWin takes account of this when determining sample sizes for operations, but just leaves gaps when graphing.

Move the cursor bar to the first observation of Cons and press Enter. A little window pops up allowing you to enter a new value. Type 887, press OK or Enter:

and you're on the next observation. Change the next three observations to 890, 891, 894. Repeat this until you have entered all observations, as in:

		Cons	Inflat		
1955-	1	887.	-.465		
1955-	2	890.	-.382		
1955-	3	891.	-.202		
1955-	4	894.	.196		
1956-	1	897.	.536		
1956-	2	895.	1.75		
1956-	3	894.	2.34		
1956-	4	892.	2.13		
1957-	1	890.	2.072		
1957-	2	889.	1.978		
1957-	3	890.	1.76		
1957-	4	887.	1.18		
1958-	1	887.	.711		
1958-	2	888.	.416		
1958-	3	889.	-.256		
1958-	4	887.	-.568		

To document each variable, position the cursor on the variable name and press ↵, or double-click on the variable name. To return to the Results window, click on Windows and select Results: you may wish to shrink the database to minimize first (or restore).

Tip   After conversion or entering new data, it is useful to do a graphic inspection which can help to find mistakes.

See Figure 5.1 for the two variables created in this tutorial.

The next important task is to save the database to disk. Losing data can be disastrous, and it is best to save it as soon as possible (and make backup copies!). But before moving to §5.2 to see how to save the results of your efforts, we consider data entry by another way. We suggest that you read the next section, but there is no need at this stage to enter the numbers again: you can highlight them in the database and use Edit/copy to put them on the clipboard, then paste to the results window if you wish: the next section explains.

5.1.2 Using the clipboard; using GiveWin as editor

To get data into a human-readable file we need the services of an editor, and the Results window will do that job. To avoid typing the data again, select all observations in the database: put the mouse down on the first observation of Cons, then, while keeping the left mouse button down, move to the last observation of Inflat. The screen should look like the capture below.

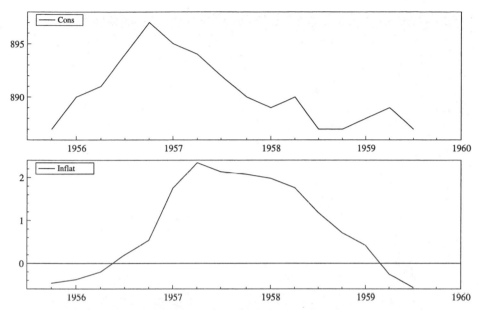

Figure 5.1   Check of Cons and Inflat.

The bottom left of the status bar gives the current selection. The right panel (887 here)
still gives the data value under the cursor. Click on the copy icon (shown as two pages

on the toolbar) to copy the data to the clipboard.   Next, set focus to the Results window, and click on the paste icon, as shown here:

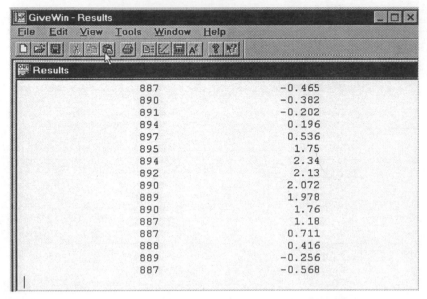

Precisely the same operations would have worked between Excel and GiveWin. Of course it is also possible to copy and paste directly between an Excel spreadsheet and a GiveWin database. The data set in this format is ordered by observation: each line has an observation (the variables are in columns).

Comment can be added to the data by putting double forward slashes (/ /) at the start of each comment line. When reading a human-readable data file, GiveWin skips all the lines starting with / / or a semicolon. If you wish, add some comments to the data here.

The next step is to save the contents of the Results window. Type Alt+f and then a to execute Save as on the File menu using the Results (*.out) file type. Enter TESTO.DAT for the filename. If the file already exists you can choose between renaming or overwriting. The human-readable data file has been created. Loading the created file is considered in §5.3.4, after we have learned how to save the database.

5.2 From GiveWin to disk

With new data entered as in §5.1.1, it is most convenient to save the database in the GiveWin format. GiveWin uses two files for its data storage. The first is an information file, which has the .IN7 extension. The second holds the data in binary (not human-readable) form, and has the .BN7 extension.

Select File/Save as/GiveWin data (*.IN7). Enter test in the save file dialog. The Database selection dialog pops up, enabling you to save a subset of the database. As you can see, the default is the whole database: Cons and Inflat are already marked, and the full sample period is entered. We will not change this, and press OK:

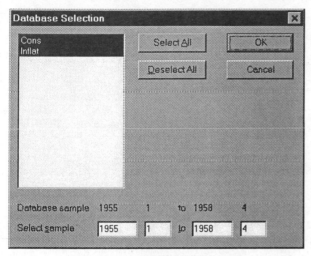

This results in the disk files TEST.IN7/TEST.BN7 being created. The GiveWin format preserves data documentation entered in the database, and the file documentation. These can be modified in a later run of GiveWin.

For completeness, we also save the data in the Excel spreadsheet format, and in plain ASCII format. Select File/Save as/XLS [Excel 2.1]; test in the save file dialog, the remainder is the same. This creates TEST.XLS. Next repeat the process for File/Save as/Data by variable (this is a human-readable file), creating TEST.DAT. The data can be ordered by variable, or by observation (see below and §8.1.3 for the difference between ordering by observation and by variable).

5.3 From disk to GiveWin

This section discusses the three main types of file which can be loaded directly into GiveWin. Consult Chapter 8 for additional information on the file formats and further examples.

5.3.1 Loading GiveWin files

This is the simplest way of getting data into GiveWin. So once you have your data from another format loaded into GiveWin, you might wish to save it in the GiveWin format, and use that from then onwards. An example was given in the first tutorial, where we loaded the tutorial data file DATA.IN7/DATA.BN7. Try loading the TEST.IN7 file which was created earlier.

5.3.2 Open **and file types**

The file type entry on the Open dialog, specifies which types of file GiveWin can load:

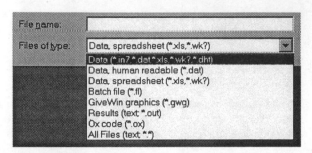

The Data (*.in7,*.dat,*.xls,*.wk?,*.dht) entry lists all the data types together for convenience. When loading a file using this type, GiveWin will look at the file extension to determine the type of data file. If the extension is .dat, or does not match any of the listed extensions, it will be treated as data with load information.

To read human readable (ASCII) files which have no sample information, you must use Data, human readable.

When loading an .in7 file as text, using Results (text; *.out) or All files (text; *.*), the file is opened as a text file:

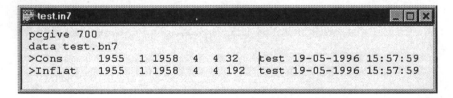

5.3.3 Loading spreadsheet files

A test file called TEST.XLS was created above. To load it in GiveWin, select File/Open/Data (*.in7,*.dat,*.xls,*.wk?,*.dht), and select the file. The file is loaded directly into GiveWin.

Occasionally, GiveWin cannot extract all load information from the spreadsheet file. Then use file type Spreadsheet (*.xls,*.wk?), in which case an additional dialog pops up for you to confirm the information GiveWin derived from the .XLS file:

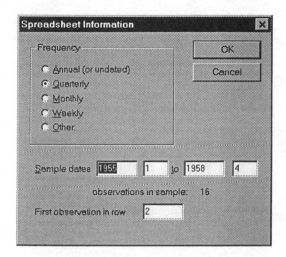

This dialog is offered to cover the cases in which GiveWin cannot work out the correct information (but could also be used to read a subsample). This is what the file would look like in Excel (try to load it if you own a copy), for the first five observations:

	A	B	C
1		Cons	Inflat
2	1955-1	887	-0.465
3	1955-2	890	-0.382
4	1955-3	891	-0.202
5	1955-4	894	0.196
6	1956-1	897	0.536

This illustrates what GiveWin expects:

- ordered by observation (that is, variables are in columns);
- columns with variables are labelled;
- there is an unlabelled column with the dates (as a text field), in the form year–period, for example, 1980–1 (or: 1980Q1 1980P1 1980:1 etc.);
- the data form a contiguous sample.

More details are in Chapter 8. However, switching between programs using Windows facilities with copying and pasting is usually the easiest approach to entering data that already exist in another program.

5.3.4 Loading a human-readable (ASCII) file

Two human-readable data files were created in this chapter, one by copying to the results window, and saving as TESTO.DAT (ordered by observations), and TEST.DAT at the end of §5.2 (ordered by variable).

To load TEST.DAT into GiveWin, use File/Open/Data, human-readable. After selecting the correct file (TEST.DAT), we are confronted with a Data file information dialog:

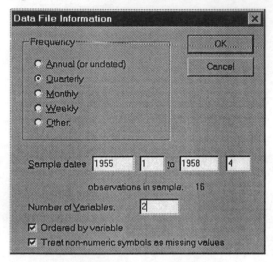

Part of this dialog first occurred in §5.1.1. Here we have to enter the same information so that GiveWin can correctly create the database and read the data file. Type 2 in the Number of variables field. Select quarterly data (Alt+q). Then Alt+s for the first sample field, type 1955, Tab, type 1, Tab, type 1958, Tab again and type 4. Finally specify the number of variables as 2. Remember that the ordering was by variable, which is the default in this dialog.

Tip   It is all too easy to specify the wrong ordering. GiveWin cannot detect this, but graphs of the data will normally show the problem.

Press the OK button (or click it with the mouse). To supply or alter a variable name, double click on the column-head box and enter Cons, then Inflat. View the database or graph the data to check the results.

5.4 Adding variables using the clipboard

Often one wishes to lift variables out of other data files, and add them to the current database. GiveWin supports this operation through copy and paste, provided the frequency matches and the samples overlap. You can select individual variables from an .IN7/.BN7 data set, or add them from a human-readable file. Once created, the sample period of the database is fixed, but can be extended if required as shown in the next section.

Let us try to append the INC variable from the tutorial data set to our database. Select File/Open/GiveWin data (*.IN7) file, choose DATA.IN7 on the file open dialog, and press Enter to accept. Highlight the observations on INC from 1955(1) to 1958(4) only, and then press the two-pages icon to copy to the clipboard. Now set focus to the test database, put the cursor on the empty field at 1955-1, next to Inflat, and press the paste icon. This copies the data, and the new variable gets the name Var3, which is easily changed.

5.5 Extending the sample period

Once the database has been created within GiveWin, it has a fixed sample period. However, it is possible to add observations before the current sample start, or after the sample end. Sometimes, you collect new observations on an existing variable, and wish to add them to the observations you already have in your .IN7/.BN7 files. Fortunately this can be achieved easily.

Suppose we wish to add a year of data at the beginning and at the end of the test data created in §5.2. Remember that the data in TEST.IN7 (and corresponding TEST.BN7) have a sample period of 1955 (1) to 1958 (4).

Focus on the database and select Edit/Extend Sample. Fill this in as follows: 4 observations at the start and 4 at the end.

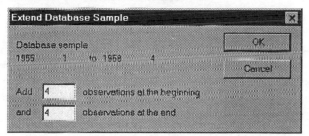

Press OK to accept. You can paste the relevant data on the variables into TEST.IN7/TEST.BN7 from the database DATA as described in §5.4 to replace the missing values for 1954 and 1959 with those observations. Don't forget to save any altered database afterwards; you can exclude any unwanted variables or observations from saving by unmarking them in the database selection dialog.

This completes our treatment of data input and output. The remainder of the tutorials will use either data that is provided with GiveWin or artificial data created inside GiveWin. After that you will have your own data to analyse; we hope that GiveWin's ample facilities allow you to enter, edit, save and document your data easily and quickly.

Chapter 6

Tutorial on Data Transformation

We briefly described the Calculator and Algebra in Chapter 2. Here we explore the transformation and data generation possibilities. Along the way, we round off the options in the Tools menu by looking at the Tail probabilities dialog.

If you are not inside GiveWin at the moment, restart and load the tutorial data set DATA.IN7/DATA.BN7.

6.1 Calculator

The calculator enables easy manipulation of the variables in the database, and is a convenient way to write algebra expressions.

The aim is to build a valid algebra expression in the expression window (without the assignment part and the terminating semi-colon). All successful transformations are logged in the Results window, from where they can be cut and pasted into an algebra file for later use if desired. Advanced algebra is discussed in the next section, whereas Chapter 9 has a more formal description of the language.

Suppose, for example, that you have selected the variable called CONS (we use the artificial data set again), and then pressed the log button. Then the expression will read log(CONS). When pressing evaluate (the = sign), the logarithm of CONS will be computed. Now you have to assign the new variable a name, with LCONS as the suggestion made by GiveWin. If you accept this suggestion, LCONS will be added to the database. If LCONS already exists, GiveWin will ask whether you wish to overwrite the existing variable.

If you have ticked the Zoom check box, you also have to select a sample period over which you wish to compute log(CONS). If you create a new variable in this way, it will be set to the missing value (-9999.99) outside the sample. If you overwrite an existing variable, it will be left untouched outside the sample period.

Examples using the calculator were given in Chapter 2. Some additional examples follow here.

First, creating a lag: select CONS, click on lag, specify 4 (to create a four-period lag) in the lag length dialog, OK to accept, and click on the button with the = symbol at

56

which point a suggested name (CONS_4) appears in a small window, to accept and the created variable is added to the database. In general, however, it is unnecessary to create lags for modelling this way.

Next, to create a step dummy of the 0-1 variety for the oil crisis: click on dummy, then enter 1973 3 in the Zero before part (leave the Zero after edit field unchanged, so the 1 extends to the end of the sample; a capture of the dialog was shown on page 19), press OK and click on = (or $\underline{C}$ to clear the expression) and specify the name s1973p3.

Third, a complex example: to create the five-period moving average of CONS:

$$\frac{1}{5} \sum_{i=0}^{4} \text{CONS}_{t-i}.$$

Select CONS in the database, locate movingavg in the function list, double click on it to see movingavg (CONS, LAG, LEAD). Replace LAG by 4 and LEAD by 0. Click on =, and specify the name MA40CONS. To create the moving average centred around the current observation (i.e. using two lags, the current value and two leads), specify movingavg(CONS, 2, 2). Note that this variable lagged two periods is the same as MA40CONS.

Other operations are equally simple. To create an Almon polynomial in INC of 2nd order over eight lags (producing three terms): Click on INC, and then double click on almon, to get the expression almon (INC, LAG, POWER). Change this to almon (INC, 8, 0) to create the first Almon variable. Call this A0INC. Repeat this to create A1INC as almon (INC, 8, 1) and A2INC as almon (INC, 8, 2). They are computed using

$$\sum_{i=0}^{8} (9-i)^j x(t-i) / \sum_{i=0}^{8} (9-i)^j \quad \text{for } j = 0, 1, 2,$$

and eight initial observations are lost. Graph these to see how collinear they are.

To create the price level from INFLAT as our final example, we need to integrate INFLAT. This is easily done using the cum or stock function. First highlight INFLAT, then double click on the cum function to cumulate. Press = to accept the expression cum (INFLAT), call it P, so that $P_t = P_{t-1}$+INFLAT is created (graph it and see). Another way to create this is selecting INFLAT, but clicking on the stock function instead. Replace ARVAL (one minus the autoregressive coefficient) by 0, and INIT (the initial value) by 0. Call this SINFLAT, and check that P and SINFLAT are identical. If you wanted P equal to 100 in 1970(1), say, when it is 86.28879985, select the same options but replace the INIT argument of stock with 13.71120015, which will set P = 100 in 1970(1).

6.2 Advanced algebra

6.2.1 Introduction

Algebra allows us to do transformations by typing formulae as described in Chapter 2. These are then executed by GiveWin. A wide range of functions is available and algebra formulae can be saved and reused. In this section we will only give examples; algebra is documented in Chapter 9.

All the code written by the calculator makes up valid algebra code as just noted. The algebra editor is activated by selecting Tools/Algebra (Alt+t,a), the short-cut key Alt+a, or the algebra toolbar button.

Algebra uses database variables as follows: if a left-hand variable is already in the database it will be overwritten, otherwise it will be created. Variables on the right must exist, possibly because of preceding lines of algebra code. As noted, algebra is case-sensitive, meaning that LCONS, LCons and lcons refer to three different variables. Algebra code is logged to the Results window.

Tip Double-click on a function in the function list or variable in the variable list to paste it into the editor. This saves typing.

Consider the insample function, which has four arguments: startyear, startperiod, endyear, endperiod. It returns 1 (or TRUE: everything which is not 0 is TRUE) if the observation under consideration falls within the sample, otherwise it returns 0 (FALSE). The conditional assignment works as follows: the conditional statement (the 'if' part) is followed by a question mark and the 'then' part, which is followed by a colon and the 'else' part. Read:

```
i1980p1 = insample(1980, 1, 1980, 1) ?  1 :  0;
```

as: i1980p1 takes on the value 1 for the observations which are in the specified sample, and the value 0 for the other observations. Note that exactly the same result can be obtained by writing i1980p1 = insample(1980, 1, 1980, 1);.

An error message pops up if you make a mistake. The error can be corrected on returning to the algebra editor.

6.2.2 Database for advanced algebra

Select File/New to create a database with 600 observations, using frequency one.

6.2.3 Statistical distributions

We shall first look at some graphs of densities and corresponding distribution functions. Most often we work with continuous density functions, and it is assumed that you are familiar with the basic principles (the PcGive book discusses statistical theory). For example, the standard normal density is defined as

$$f_X(x) = \frac{1}{\sqrt{2\pi}} e^{-\frac{1}{2}x^2},$$

with cumulative distribution function (CDF)

$$F_X(x) = \int_{-\infty}^{x} f_X(u)\, du.$$

This integral cannot be written explicitly for the normal distribution. F is a nondecreasing function and:

$$F_X(-\infty) = 0, \ F_X(\infty) = 1.$$

If X has a continuous distribution, then the expectation of X is:

$$E[X] = \int_{-\infty}^{\infty} u f_X(u)\, du.$$

We write $X \sim N(0,1)$ to say that the random variable X follows a standard normal distribution. Three other distributions of interest are the student-t, the F and the χ^2 distribution:

$$t(k) \qquad f_X = \frac{\Gamma(k/2+1/2)}{\Gamma(k/2)} \frac{1}{\sqrt{k\pi}} \left(1 + \frac{x^2}{k}\right)^{-k/2 - 1/2} \qquad k = 1,2,\ldots$$

$$F(m,n) \quad f_X = \frac{\Gamma(m/2+n/2)}{\Gamma(m/2)\Gamma(n/2)} \left(\frac{m}{n}\right)^{m/2} x^{m/2-1} \left(1 + \frac{m}{n}x\right)^{-m/2 - n/2} \quad \begin{array}{l} x > 0, \\ m, n = 1,\ldots \end{array}$$

$$\chi^2(k) \qquad f_X = \frac{1}{\Gamma(k/2)} \left(\frac{1}{2}\right)^{k/2} x^{k/2-1} e^{-x/2} \qquad \begin{array}{l} x > 0, \\ k = 1,2,\ldots \end{array}$$

$\Gamma(\cdot)$ is the gamma function:

$$\Gamma(u) = \int_0^{\infty} x^{u-1} e^{-x} dx \quad \text{for } u > 0.$$

For integer arguments n: $\Gamma(n+1) = n! = n(n-1)(n-2) \cdots 1$. Most test statistics in PcGive have one of these distributions (but often only approximately or in large samples).

We compute 600 values from $N(0,1)$, $t(2)$, $\chi^2(3)$ and $F(3,2)$, over a range of -6 to 6, in steps of .02. This is the variable called i in the first line of algebra. The algebra code is in the file TUTDIST.ALG; the section for the densities is:

```
normal = densn(i);
chi = (i > 0) ? denschi(i,3);
student = denst(i,2);
F = (i > 0) ? densf(i,3,2);
```

Run the code from TUTDIST.ALG, and do a cross plot of each of the four variables against i, as in Figure 6.1. This shows the four densities.

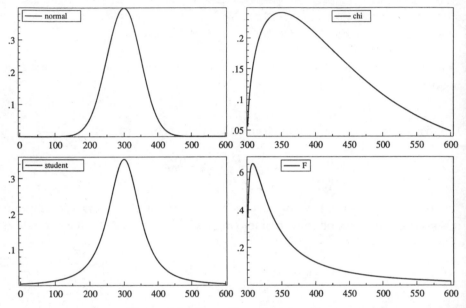

Figure 6.1   Some important densities.

It is also possible to evaluate the densities directly, instead of using the built in functions. Note in the second line that we write $-(i^2)$; $-i^2$ would be equivalent to $(-i)^2$, as the unary minus operator has a higher precedence than power (see Table 9.3 in Chapter 9). The $\Gamma(\cdot)$ function is not available in the algebra, but the $\log\Gamma(\cdot)$ is and we use the fact that $\Gamma(\cdot) = \exp(\log\Gamma(\cdot))$.

```
normal = exp(-(i^2) / 2) / sqrt(2 * PI);
chi = (i > 0) ? 1 / exp(loggamma(1.5)) * 0.5 ^ 1.5
      * i ^ 0.5 * exp(-i / 2);
student = exp(loggamma(1.5) - loggamma(1)) /
      (sqrt(2 * PI) * (1 + i^2 / 2) ^ 1.5);
F = (i > 0) ? exp(loggamma(2.5) - loggamma(1.5)
      - loggamma(1)) * 1.5 ^ 1.5 * i ^ 0.5
      / (1 + 1.5 * i) ^ 2.5;
```

To translate the densities into approximate CDFs, the following code is used in TUT-DIST.ALG to cumulate and scale the outcomes (which are in increasing order given our choice of i for the densities):

```
cnormal = cum(normal) / (NOBS/12);
cchi = cum(chi) / (NOBS/12);
cstudent = cum(student) / (NOBS/12);
cF = cum(F) / (NOBS/12);
```

We have actually performed a numerical integration of the densities! At each point we computed the height of the function, and added these up. Since the width of each bar is only 1/50, we have to divide by 50 (the surface of a bar equals *height* × *width*).

It can be noted from Figure 6.1 that the $F(3,2)$ distribution has no variance: it approaches 1 very slowly. The same holds for the $t(2)$ distribution.

The approximate 75% critical values as read from the database are:

$$N(0,1) \quad .66$$
$$t(2) \quad .86$$
$$\chi^2(3) \quad 4.1$$
$$F(3,2) \quad 3.16$$

The accuracy turns out to be quite good. If we compute the p-values using Tools/Tail probability we find:

```
N(0,1,1-sided) =  0.66 [0.2546]
t(2,1-sided)   =  0.86 [0.2402]
Chi^2(3)       =  4.1  [0.2509]
F(3, 2)        =  3.16 [0.2496]
```

This dialog gives $P(X > x)$ when 2-sided is not marked, in which case we would ideally get p values of 25%.

6.2.4 Random number generators

The random number generators in GiveWin can be used to illustrate statistical concepts, and to give examples of a wide range of commonly used processes. The main generators are for the uniform distribution (all other distributions can be derived from this), and the standard normal distribution. In addition, GiveWin provides functions to draw from the t, χ^2, and F distributions. Other distributions could be derived if desired. An alternative way to draw from a $\chi^2(k)$, for example, is to compute the sum of k squared standard normals. Ripley (1987) discusses these issues.

The following experiments use 10 000 observations, but you could keep on using the database with 600 observations. Otherwise create a new database with 10 thousand annual observations. Draw from the $N(0,1)$, $t(100)$, $\chi^2(3)$, and $F(3,100)$ distributions, and compute the probabilities (using the correct distributions) to get a value less than the observed numbers:

```
phi = rann();
stu = rant(100);
chi = ranchi(3);
fdi = ranf(3, 100);
```

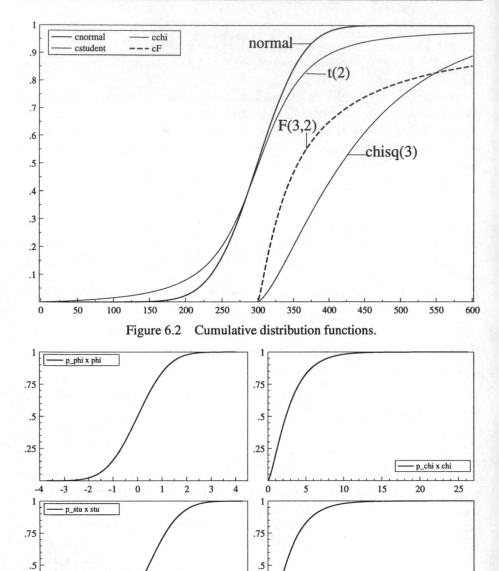

Figure 6.2   Cumulative distribution functions.

Figure 6.3   Cumulative distribution functions.

```
p_phi = 1 - tailn(phi);
p_stu = 1 - tailt(stu, 100);
```

```
p_chi = 1 - tailchi(chi, 3);
p_fdi = 1 - tailf(fdi, 3, 100);
```

The algebra code is in the file TUTRAN1.ALG. When using 10 000 observations, the computations may take a little while.

Using these data, we can draw the cumulative distribution functions as in Figure 6.2. In this case we used a t and F distribution with finite variance. You could try the distributions of §6.2.3: there will be some large outliers, extending the scale of the graphs.

A check of the random number generators can be based on the probabilities. Sort each vector of probabilities, and corresponding random numbers with it:

```
_sortby(p_phi, phi);
_sortby(p_stu, stu);
_sortby(p_chi, chi);
_sortby(p_fdi, fdi);
```

Figure 6.4 shows that the probabilities form a straight line. A plot of the sorted random numbers look like a mirror image of Figure 6.3. Alternatively, graph the histogram and densities of phi, stu, chi and fdi to see sample analogues of the distributions.

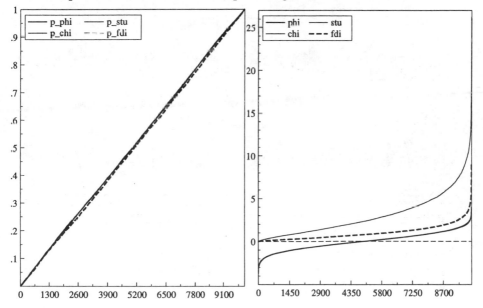

Figure 6.4   Check on CDFs.

6.2.5 Generating data

Finally, we shall generate data on various autoregressive and related processes. The database is assumed to consist of 600 'annual' observations, as in §6.2.3. The file TUTRAN2.ALG contains the algebra code used in this section.

Consider the following examples (note that the roots in the MA(2) process are -0.87 and -0.23):

$$\begin{aligned}
&\text{white noise} &&\epsilon_t \sim \mathsf{N}(0,1), \\
&\text{AR}(1) &&y_t = 0.6y_{t-1} + \epsilon_t, \\
&\text{AR}(2) &&y_t = 0.4y_{t-1} - 0.7y_{t-2} + \epsilon_t, \\
&\text{MA}(2) &&y_t = \epsilon_t + 1.1\epsilon_{t-1} + 0.2\epsilon_{t-2}, \\
&\text{ARMA}(2,2) &&y_t = -1.4y_{t-1} - 0.5y_{t-2} + \epsilon_t - 0.2\epsilon_{t-1} - 0.1\epsilon_{t-2}, \\
&\text{ARCH} &&y_t = \sigma_t\epsilon_t, \quad \sigma_t^2 = 1 + 0.6y_{t-1}^2.
\end{aligned}$$

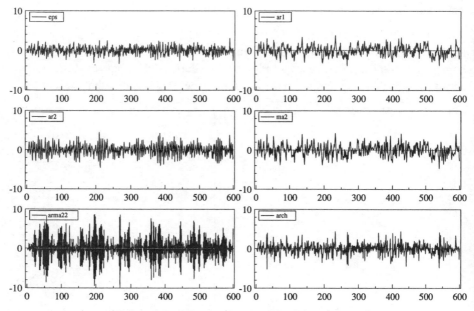

Figure 6.5   Time series graphs of 6 processes.

The middle four processes are used as examples in Priestley (1981). For the ARCH (autoregressive conditional heteroscedasticity) process, see, for example, Harvey (1993). The following algebra code generates a sample from the six processes:

```
ranseed(-1);
eps = rann();
ar1 = year() >= 3 ? .6 * lag(ar1,1) + eps : 0;
ar2 = year() >= 3 ? .4 * lag(ar2,1)
      - .7*lag(ar2,2) + eps : 0;
ma2 = eps + 1.1 * lag(eps,1) + .2 * lag(eps,2);
arma22 = year() >= 3 ? -1.4 * lag(arma22,1)
       - .5 * lag(arma22,2) + eps
       - .2 * lag(eps,1) - .1 * lag(eps,2) : 0;
arch = year() >= 3 ? sqrt(1 + 0.6
       * lag(arch,1)^2) * eps : 0;
```

The ranseed() function sets the seed of the random number generator, an argument of -1 resets the seed to the default value. The variable eps is $N(0,1)$ and is reused in each process. The autoregressive parts use conditional statements. If the year is $\geq$ 3 (we use annual data, so this corresponds to an observation index $\geq$ 3), the part following the ? is executed. For the first two observations the value zero is used. In this way a variable can be integrated safely (without the conditional statement all observations would have the missing value). The test `year()` `>= 3` could also be written as `insample(3,1,600,1)` or `lag(eps,2)` `!= MISSING`. Try to understand and compare these alternatives.

Figure 6.5 graphs the results, adjusting the axes to give the same vertical range. The correlograms and spectral densities are given in Figure 6.6.

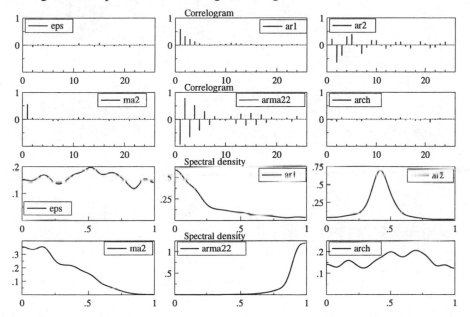

Figure 6.6   Correlograms and spectral densities of six processes.

The remaining examples correspond to the equation:

$$y_t = \alpha + \beta y_{t-1} + \mu t + \epsilon_t, \quad \epsilon_t \sim N(0,1),$$

using parameter values:

z1…z3:	$\alpha = 0, \beta = 1, \mu = 0$	$\alpha = 0, \beta = .9, \mu = 0$	$\alpha = 0, \beta = .5,$ $\mu = 0$
m1…m3:	$\alpha = .1, \beta = 1, \mu = 0$	$\alpha = .1, \beta = .9, \mu = 0$	$\alpha = .1, \beta = .5,$ $\mu = 0$
t1…t3:	$\alpha = .1, \beta = 1, \mu = .001$	$\alpha = .1, \beta = .9, \mu = .001$	$\alpha = .1, \beta = .5,$ $\mu = .001$

The algebra code uses the eps variable created above.

```
z1 = year() >= 3 ?  1 * lag(z1,1) + eps : 0;
z2 = year() >= 3 ? .9 * lag(z2,1) + eps : 0;
z3 = year() >= 3 ? .5 * lag(z3,1) + eps : 0;
m1 = year() >= 3 ? .1 + 1 * lag(m1,1) + eps : 0;
m2 = year() >= 3 ? .1 +.9 * lag(m2,1) + eps : 0;
m3 = year() >= 3 ? .1 +.5 * lag(m3,1) + eps : 0;
t1 = year() >= 3 ? .1 +.001*trend() + 1*lag(t1,1) + eps : 0;
t2 = year() >= 3 ? .1 +.001*trend() +.9*lag(t2,1) + eps : 0;
t3 = year() >= 3 ? .1 +.001*trend() +.5*lag(t3,1) + eps : 0;
```

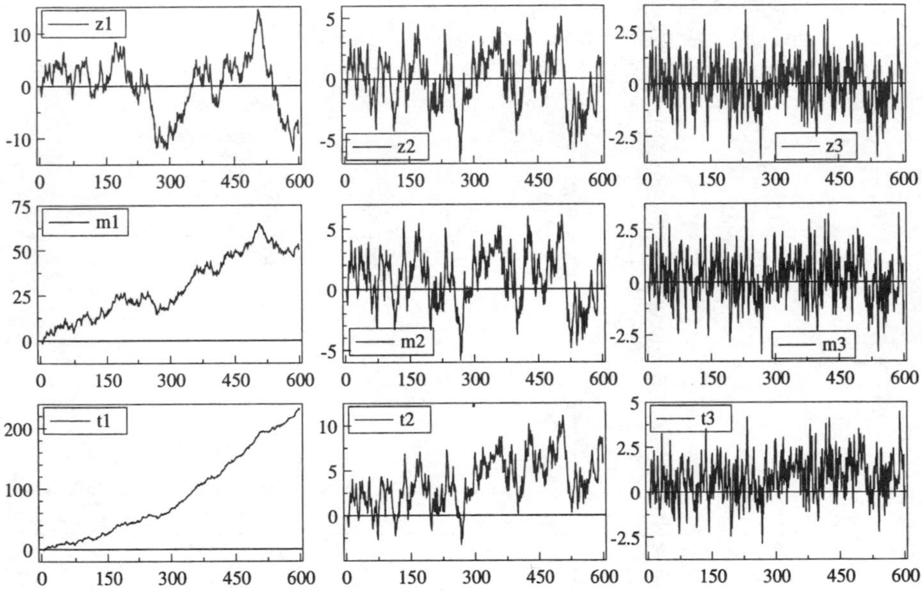

Figure 6.7   AR(1) with various parameter values.

Figure 6.7 clearly shows the impact of the different parameter values on the behaviour of the functions.

6.2.6 Smoothing data

As our last tutorial example, we show how the natural cubic spline function can be used to fit missing values. Load the tutorial data set DATA.IN7.

First edit the CONS variable to set the observations for the years 1958, 1968 and 1978 to missing values (for each year: select the four observations, press Enter, set to Missing value, press Enter again, and apply to the whole selection). Afterwards, make sure that you do not save this modified database.

Select the Cross plot graphics dialog, and do a cross plot of CONS against time (so there is no need to choose an X variable), adding a Cubic spline smooth using all three bandwidth settings. The results should be similar to Figure 6.8. The label of the spline line gives the equivalent number of parameters (comparable to the number of variables used in a linear regression). So we see that a bandwidth of 1600 corresponds to nearly 10 parameters (it also corresponds to the Hodrick-Prescott filter, see §7.5.2), whereas automatic bandwidth selection is much less smooth, with an equivalence to 47 parameters.

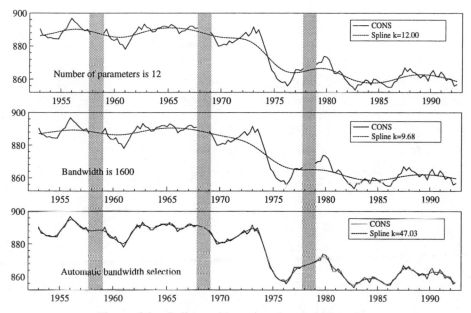

Figure 6.8   Splines with various bandwidth settings.

The following algebra code creates the three smooths in the database (see §9.2.11):

```
sp1CONS = smooth_sp(CONS,        0, sp1CONS);
sp3CONS = smooth_sp(CONS,       12, sp3CONS);
sp2CONS = smooth_sp(CONS, -1600, sp2CONS);
```

You could try to add the appropriate variable to each graph by selecting the area (left mouse button), and then using Add Variable. When done correctly, each added variable should exactly cover the pre-existing spline.

Part III

GiveWin Manuals

Chapter 7

GiveWin Statistics

GiveWin provides many convenient graphical options for prior data analysis. For simplicity we denote the selected variable by x_t, $t = 1, \ldots, T$. This chapter summarizes the underlying formulae. The following graphs are available:

7.1 Actual values and cross plots

Actual values gives a graph for each selected variable, showing the variable over time. The All cross plots option gives cross plots between all selected variables (omitting redundant cross plots).

7.2 Correlogram

This plots the series $\{\hat{r}_j^*\}$ where $\hat{r}_j^*$ is the correlation coefficient between x_t and x_{t-j}. The length of the correlogram is specified by the user, leading to a figure which shows $(\hat{r}_1^*, \hat{r}_2^*, \ldots, \hat{r}_s^*)$ plotted against $(1, 2, \ldots, s)$ where for any j when x is any chosen variable:

$$\hat{r}_j^* = \frac{\sum_{t=j+1}^{T} (x_t - \bar{x}_0)(x_{t-j} - \bar{x}_j)}{\sqrt{\sum_{t=j+1}^{T} (x_t - \bar{x}_0)^2 \sum_{t=j+1}^{T} (x_{t-j} - \bar{x}_j)^2}}. \tag{7.1}$$

Here $\bar{x}_0 = \frac{1}{T-j} \sum_{t=j+1}^{T} x_t$ is the sample mean of x_t, $t = j+1, \ldots, T$, and $\bar{x}_j = \frac{1}{T-j} \sum_{t=j+1}^{T} x_{t-j}$ is the sample mean of x_{t-j}, so that $\hat{r}_j^*$ corresponds to a correlation coefficient proper. Note the difference with the definition of the sample autocorrelations $\{\hat{r}_j\}$ in (7.2) below. This difference tends to be small, and vanishes asymptotically.

If there are missing values in the data series, the correlogram uses data starting from the first valid observation, and stopping at the first missing value thereafter.

71

7.3 Spectral density

The estimated spectral density is a smoothed function of the sample autocorrelations $\{\hat{r}_j\}$, defined as:

$$\hat{r}_j = \frac{\sum_{t=j+1}^{T} (x_t - \bar{x})(x_{t-j} - \bar{x})}{\sum_{t=1}^{T} (x_t - \bar{x})^2}, \quad j = 0, \ldots, T-1, \tag{7.2}$$

using the full sample mean $\bar{x} = \frac{1}{T}\sum_{t=1}^{T} x_t$. The sample spectral density is then defined as:

$$s(\omega) = \frac{1}{2\pi} \sum_{j=-(T-1)}^{T-1} K(j)\hat{r}_{|j|} \cos(j\omega), \quad 0 \le \omega \le \pi, \tag{7.3}$$

where $|\cdot|$ takes the absolute value, so that, for example, $\hat{r}_{|-1|} = \hat{r}_1$. The $K(\cdot)$ function is called the *lag window*. GiveWin uses the Parzen window:

$$
\begin{aligned}
K(j) &= 1 - 6\left(\tfrac{j}{m}\right)^2 + 6\left|\tfrac{j}{m}\right|^3, & \left|\tfrac{j}{m}\right| \le 0.5, \\
&= 2\left(1 - \left|\tfrac{j}{m}\right|\right)^3, & 0.5 \le \left|\tfrac{j}{m}\right| \le 1.0, \\
&= 0, & \left|\tfrac{j}{m}\right| > 1.
\end{aligned}
\tag{7.4}
$$

We have that $K(-j) = K(j)$, so that the sign of j does not matter $(\cos(x) = \cos(-x))$. The $\hat{r}_j$s are based on fewer observations as j increases. The window function attaches decreasing weights to the autocorrelations, with zero weight for $j > m$. The parameter m is called the *lag truncation parameter*. In GiveWin this is taken to be the same as the chosen length of the correlogram: selecting, for example, $s = 12$ there results in $m = 12$. The larger m, the less smooth the spectrum becomes, but the lower the bias. The spectrum is evaluated at 128 points between 0 and π. For more information see Priestley (1981) and Granger and Newbold (1986).

If there are missing values in the data series, the spectral density uses data starting from the first valid observation, and stopping at the first missing value thereafter.

7.4 Histogram, estimated density and distribution

Given a data set $\{x_t\} = (x_1 \ldots x_T)$ which are observations on a random variable X; write z_t for the standardized xs:

$$z_t = \frac{x_t - \bar{x}}{\hat{\sigma}_x}, \quad \text{where } \bar{x} = \frac{1}{T}\sum_{t=1}^{T} x_t \quad \text{and } \hat{\sigma}_x = \sqrt{\frac{1}{T}\sum_{t=1}^{T}(x_t - \bar{x})}.$$

The range of $\{z_t\}$ is divided into N intervals of length h with h defined below. Then the proportion of z_t in each interval constitutes the histogram; the sum of the proportions is unity on the scaling in GiveWin. The density can be estimated as a smoothed function of the histogram using a normal or Gaussian kernel. This can then be summed ('integrated') to obtain the estimated cumulative distribution function (CDF).

Denote the actual density of Z at z by $f_z(z)$. A non-parametric estimate of the density is obtained from the sample by:

$$\widehat{f_z(z)} = \frac{1}{Th} \sum_{t=1}^{T} K\left(\frac{z - z_t}{h}\right),$$ (7.5)

where h is the *window width* or smoothing parameter, and $K(\cdot)$ is a *kernel* such that:

$$\int_{-\infty}^{\infty} K(x)\,\mathrm{d}x = 1.$$

GiveWin sets

$$h = 1.06\hat{\sigma}_z/T^{0.2}$$

as a default and uses the standard normal density for $K(\cdot)$:

$$K\left(\frac{z - z_t}{h}\right) = \frac{1}{\sqrt{2\pi}} \exp\left[-\frac{1}{2}\left(\frac{z - z_t}{h}\right)^2\right].$$ (7.6)

The default window width is used when the dialog option is set to Default bars. Alternatively, it is possible to directly choose the number of bars, in which case, the more bars, the less smooth the density estimate will be.

$\widehat{f_z(z)}$ is usually calculated for 128 values of z, but since direct evaluation can be somewhat expensive in computer time, a fast Fourier transform is used (we are grateful to Dr. Silverman for permission to use his algorithm). The estimated CDF of Z can be derived from $\widehat{f_z(z)}$; this is shown with a standard normal CDF for comparison. An excellent reference on density function estimation is Silverman (1986).

7.5 Regression lines and smooths

The cross plots option allows for various types of regression lines to be drawn. A single regression line draws the OLS estimates $\hat{\alpha}$ and $\hat{\beta}$ in

$$y_t = \hat{\alpha} + \hat{\beta} x_t, \quad t = 1,\dots T,$$

assuming that y_t and x_t are the selected variables. The distinction between sequential and recursive regression lines is easily explained using three lines. Divide the sample in three parts: $1,\dots,T/3, T/3+1,\dots,2T/3$ and $2T/3+1,\dots,T$, then:

$$
\text{sequential} \quad
\begin{array}{ll}
\text{line 1} & y_t = \hat{\alpha}_1 + \hat{\beta}_1 x_t, \quad t = 1, \ldots T/3, \\
\text{line 2} & y_t = \hat{\alpha}_2 + \hat{\beta}_2 x_t, \quad t = T/3 + 1, \ldots, 2T/3, \\
\text{line 3} & y_t = \hat{\alpha}_3 + \hat{\beta}_3 x_t, \quad t = 2T/3 + 1, \ldots, T,
\end{array}
$$

$$
\text{recursive} \quad
\begin{array}{ll}
\text{line 1} & y_t = \hat{\alpha}_1 + \hat{\beta}_1 x_t, \quad t = 1, \ldots T/3, \\
\text{line 2} & y_t = \hat{\alpha}_4 + \hat{\beta}_4 x_t, \quad t = 1, \ldots, 2T/3, \\
\text{line 3} & y_t = \hat{\alpha} + \hat{\beta} x_t, \quad t = 1, \ldots, T.
\end{array}
$$

Some examples were given in Chapter 3.

7.5.1 Kernel smooth

As a first step towards non-parametric regression, we start with a cross plot of y_t and x_t, with x_t along the horizontal axis. Divide the x-axis in N intervals, and compute the average y-value in each interval. The resulting step function provides a non-parametric regression line: to compute $\hat{y}(x_0)$ we locate the interval on which x_0 falls, and use the mean of y in that interval as $\hat{y}$. An obvious drawback is that, if x_0 is towards the edge of an interval, most of the observations are on the other side. Solve this by centring the interval in x_0. This still gives as much weight to points far away as to points nearby. In line with the smoothing functions (kernels) in the spectrum and density estimates, we use a density function to take a weighted average.

The non-parametric estimate of y is obtained from

$$
\hat{y}_h(x) = \left(\sum_{t=1}^{T} K\left(\frac{x - x_t}{h} \right) \right)^{-1} \left(\sum_{t=1}^{T} K\left(\frac{x - x_t}{h} \right) y_t \right), \tag{7.7}
$$

where as for (7.5) h is the window width, *bandwidth* or smoothing parameter, and $K(\cdot)$ is a kernel which integrates to 1. GiveWin uses the Epanechnikov kernel:

$$
\begin{array}{ll}
K(u) = & \frac{3}{4}\left(1 - u^2\right), \quad |u| \le 1, \\
= & 0, \quad\quad\quad\quad\; |u| > 1,
\end{array} \tag{7.8}
$$

which is optimal in a certain sense. The optimal bandwidth, equivalent to the default chosen for the non-parametric density estimate is:

$$
h = 0.75 \hat{\sigma}_x / T^{0.2}.
$$

The function $\hat{y}_h(\cdot)$ is computed at 128 points. As $h \to 0$, $\hat{y}_h(\cdot) \to \bar{y}$: the sample mean is the fitted value for any x. On the other hand, if $h \to \infty$ the interval goes to zero, and we fit the nearest corresponding y-value so that each data point is picked up exactly. Note, however, that the $\hat{y}(\cdot)$ function is evaluated at the T data points x_t (which is time in the absence of x). Härdle (1990) is a general reference on the subject of non-parametric regression.

There are three ways of specifying the bandwidth:

- Number of parameters
  This specifies the equivalent number of parameters (approximately comparable to the number of regressors used in a linear regression). The default is

$$\frac{3}{4} \left[\frac{(T-1)}{12} \right]^{1/2} T^{-0.2}$$

- Set
  Sets the bandwidth directly.
- Automatic
  Chooses the bandwidth by generalized cross validation (GCV). We find that choosing bandwidth using GCV or cross validation (CV) tends to undersmooth. Equation (7.9) below indicates how GCV is computed.

The kernel smooth is *not* computed using a Fourier transform, but directly, so can be slow for large T. The smooth is fitted over the whole sample including missing values inside sample, which are estimated by the fit from the smooth.

One drawback of this smooth is that, for trending lines, it behaves counter intuitively at the edges. Consider for example the left edge of the kernel smooth of a variable which is upwardly trending. Since the smooth starts as a moving average of points which are only to the right, and hence mainly higher, the left edge will have a J shape, starting above what would be fitted by eye.

7.5.2 Spline smooth

A spline is another method for smoothing a cross plot. Consider a plot of y_t, against x_t, and sort the data according to x: $a < x_{[1]} < \ldots < x_{[T]} < b$. In a spline model, the sum of squared deviations from a function g is minimized, subject to a roughness penalty:

$$\min \sum_{t=1}^{T} \left[y_t - g\left(x_{[t]}\right) \right]^2 + \alpha \int_a^b \left[g''(x) \right]^2 dx.$$

GiveWin uses a *natural cubic spline*, which is cubic because the function g is chosen as a third degree polynomial, and natural because the smooth is a straight line between a and $x_{[1]}$ and between $x_{[1]}$ and b. This avoids the end-point problem of the kernel smooth of the previous section. Two good references on splines and nonparametric regression are Green and Silverman (1994) and Hastie and Tibshirani (1994).

The α parameter is the bandwidth: the smaller α, the lower the roughness penalty, and hence the closer the smooth will track the actual data.

The spline is evaluated at the data points, where missing y values are estimated by the fit from the smooth. The spline procedure handles ties in the x variable. The algorithm used to compute the spline is of order T, and discussed extensively in Green and Silverman (1994, Chs.2,3).

For evenly spaced data (e.g. cross plot against time), the algorithm involves a Toeplitz matrix. This shows the closeness of a natural cubic spline to the Hodrick–Prescott filter which is popular in macro-economics:

	diagonal	2nd diag	3rd diag	remainder
Hodrick–Prescott	$6\alpha + 1$	-4α	α	0
spline	$6\alpha + 2/3$	$-4\alpha + 1/6$	α	0

The only difference is in this Toeplitz matrix. Since the Hodrick–Prescott filter uses $\alpha = 1600$, the smoothers from both methods are virtually identical.[1]

There are three ways of specifying the bandwidth:

- Number of parameters
  This specifies the equivalent number of parameters, k_e, (approximately comparable to the number of regressors used in a linear regression). The default is

$$\frac{3}{4} \left[\frac{(T-1)}{12} \right]^{1/2} T^{-0.2}$$

- Set
  Sets the bandwidth directly, with the default of 1600 corresponding to the Hodrick–Prescott filter.
- Automatic
  Chooses the bandwidth by generalized cross validation (GCV). We find that choosing bandwidth using GCV or cross validation (CV) tends to undersmooth. The GCV criterion is computed as:

$$GCV(\alpha) = T \left(\frac{RSS}{T - 1.25k_e + 0.5} \right). \tag{7.9}$$

We have adopted GCV instead of CV because a very good fit at one point could dominate the CV criterion.

7.6 QQ plot

Draws a QQ plot. The variable would normally hold critical values which are hypothesized to come from a certain distribution. This function then draws a cross plot of these observed values (sorted), against the theoretical quantiles. The 45° line is drawn for reference (the closer the cross plot to this line, the better the match).

---

[1] Some articles describe computation of the Hodrick–Prescott filter as involving inversion of a $T \times T$ matrix. This is clearly not the case. It is avoided in the Reinsch algorithm used for the general cross-plot smooth, and more obviously in the evenly spaced case, where all that is required is the solution of a linear system involving a banded Toeplitz matrix. Alternatively, the Kalman filter may be used, as in Koopman, Harvey, Doornik and Shephard (1995).

The following distributions are supported:

- $\chi^2(df1)$,
- $F(df1, df2)$,
- $N(0, 1)$,
- $t(df1)$,
- $\text{Uniform}(0, 1)$, resulting in a Quantile plot.

7.7 Box plot

A box plot shows the distribution of a variable in terms of its quartiles, labelled Q_1, Q_2, Q_3 (the 25%, 50% and 75% quartiles). Define the interquartile range as $IQR = 1.5(Q_3 - Q_1)$. The box plot consists of the following elements:

- a box, with horizontal lines at Q_1, Q_2 (the median) and Q_3;
- a vertical line from $Q_1 - IQR$ to $Q_3 + IQR$ (omitted inside the box);
- individual observations: all observations outside the $(Q_1 - IQR, Q_3 + IQR)$ range, plus the two observations on either end which just fall inside this range.

Chapter 8

GiveWin file formats

8.1 GiveWin data files (.IN7/.BN7)

8.1.1 The .IN7 file format

The most convenient way of storing data on disk when using GiveWin is the combination of the information (.IN7) and binary (.BN7) data file.

The information file holds the information about the data set. It has the .IN7 extension. The information file is accompanied by a binary data file. The binary data file holds the actual data, and has the .BN7 extension. The .IN7/.BN7 combination is convenient because information on sample size etc. is automatically stored. Table 8.1 lists the DATA.IN7 file.

Note GiveWin uses the same format as PcGive versions 7 and 8.

Table 8.1   DATA.IN7: information file of artificial data set.

```
pcgive 700
data data.BN7
;Tutorial Data Set:4 equation model with oil shock for PcGive
;October 1985
>CONS     1953 1 1992 3   4    32 data      10-04-1992   13:20:38.33
; Artificial consumption variable
>INC      1953 1 1992 3   4   1336 data      10-04-1992   13:20:38.33
; Artificial income variable
>INFLAT   1953 1 1992 3   4   2640 data      10-04-1992   13:20:38.33
; Artificial inflation variable
>OUTPUT   1953 1 1992 3   4   3944 data      10-04-1992   13:20:38.33
; Artificial output variable
```

The following items are found in the .IN7 file:

Identification The first line must be the file identification followed by a version number. Currently the identification is pcgive and the version is 700. This will change if new features are added to the format.

78

Data file name The second line specifies the type of file (`data`), and gives the name of the data file corresponding to the information file. Here it is a binary file, called `data.bn7`. The .BN7 extension indicates that this file is a binary file. If the specified file has the .DAT extension, it is assumed to be an ASCII (that is, human-readable) file, ordered by variable, see §8.1.3.

When *xxx*.in7 is used, and if *xxx*.bn7 exists in the same directory, the `data` statement is ignored. Else, the `data` part must specify the .BN7 file. This behaviour is new with version 1.0 of GiveWin, and allows renaming a .IN7/.BN7 pair without having to edit the .IN7 file.

Lines starting with a semicolon are comment lines, so the third line in the example is a comment line. All comment lines following the data statement are considered to document the whole file.

Variable definition The remaining entries are variable definitions. The first character (> or −) indicates the status and is described below.

All lines starting with a semicolon that follow a variable definition are comments on the variable. This documentation can be edited in the database window by selecting the variable name. When saving the database in the GiveWin format, the documentation is preserved.

There is one line defining each variable, which holds the following information:

>CONS	1953 1 1992 3	4	32	data	10−04−1992 13:20
↓	↓	↓	↓		↓
↓	sample period	frequency	address	group	date & time
name, preceded by status: active (>) or deleted (−)					

Status If the status is a minus sign, the variable is deleted (but physically still present). A deleted variable will not be loaded into GiveWin.

Variable name Maximal 11 characters. No spaces are allowed in the variable names, but names like CONS−INC, which would not be valid variable names in any programming language, are allowed.

Generation The generation is not explicitly stored in the information file, but derived from the variable name. If there is more than one entry with an identical name (also written in identical case, since Cons and CONS are different), then the first one has generation 0, the second generation 1, etc. Only the highest generation (most recent version) will be loaded into GiveWin.

Sample period The sample period consists of four numbers: *startyear*, *startperiod*, *endyear* and *endperiod*. Each variable in the data file can have a different sample period. When reading such a file into GiveWin with a still empty database, the sample containing all data will be used (missing observations will get the missing value: −9999.99).

Frequency Variables with different frequencies can be stored, but only one frequency at a time can be loaded into GiveWin.

Address Gives the physical address of the variable in the binary data file. So the first observation of CONS starts at byte 32 in data.bn7, the second at byte 40 etc. (data is stored in double precision, taking eight bytes per observation). The 32 bytes preceding every variable are a separate information block, from which a rudimentary information file can be reconstructed.

Group Variables in a file can be grouped together by the group name.

Date and time fields These give the date and time at which the variable was written. No spaces are allowed in either field.

The amount of data in the .IN7/.BN7 files is only limited by available disk space. This is usually much more than can be loaded at one time in GiveWin. C source code and object files to read .IN7/.BN7 files are available on request. Ox can read and write .IN7/.BN7 on all computer platforms.

8.1.2 The .BN7 file format

The .BN7 file is a binary file, and thus not human readable. It holds the actual data.

Each variable starts with a 32 bit signature, followed by the data in the form of 8 byte doubles. The doubles have the standard IEEE form and are stored in little endian format (the default on PC platforms).

The 32 bit signature consists of:

bytes	type	description
0-7	double	marker
8-11	int	number of observations (T)
12-23	char[12]	variable name (padded with null characters)
24-25	short int	frequency
26-27	short int	starting period
28-29	short int	starting
30-31	short int	not used

This signature is followed by $8 \times T$ bytes. The signature is always written, but never read, because all the relevant information is obtained from the .IN7 file, including the starting address of each variable. Note that int is a 32 bit signed integer, and short int a 16 bit signed integer.

8.1.3 The information and ASCII data files (.IN7/.DAT)

An information file may describe a human-readable data file which is ordered by variable. This option is especially useful for the situation where GiveWin is routinely used to process output generated by another program which cannot write binary data files. When saving data, GiveWin will always create a binary data file with accompanying information file. To attach a human-readable file to an information file, the filename following the *data* statement should have the .DAT extension (and the .BN7 file must not exist, otherwise that file is read instead). In the example of Table 8.1 the second line would read data data.DAT. Then GiveWin will assume that the data is stored in the human-readable (ASCII) data file DATA.DAT. The data must be ordered by variable, and offending words are treated as missing values (see §8.3). Apart from the *data* statement, the organization of the .IN7 file is the same as in §8.1. The value in the address field will be ignored, the date and time field may be missing.

8.2 Spreadsheet files (.XLS,.WKS,.WK1)

GiveWin can read and write the following spreadsheet files:

- Excel: .XLS files;
- Lotus: .WKS, .WK1 files;

provided the following convention is adopted:

- Ordered by observation (that is, variables are in columns).
- Columns with variables are labelled.
- There is an unlabelled column with the dates (as a string), in the form year–period (the – can actually be any single character), for example, 1980–1 (or: 1980Q1 1980P1 1980:1 etc.). This doesn't have to be the first column.
- The data form a contiguous sample (non-numeric fields are converted to missing values, so you can leave gaps for missing observations).

GiveWin can read the following types of Excel files:

- Excel 2.1;
- Excel 3.0;
- Excel 4.0.

When saving an Excel file, it is written in Excel 2.1 format.

For example, the format for writing is (this is also the optimal format for reading):

	A	B	C	D
1		CONS	INFL	DUM
2	1980-1	883	2.7	3
3	1980-2	884	3.5	5
4	1980-3	885	3.9	1
5	1980-4	889	2.6	9
6	1981-1	900	3.4	2

If these conventions are not adopted the file can still be read, but you might have to provide some additional information, such as frequency, start date and row of first observation. In the example, these are respectively 4, 1980 1, 2.

We shall give some examples to show what happens if the conventions are not adopted. The spreadsheet is displayed on the left, the GiveWin database after reading on the right. In the first example the column with dates is invalid. GiveWin assumes frequency 1 and start period 1-1 in that case, but always allows this information to be changed.

	A	B	C	D		GiveWin database		
1		aap	noot	mies		aap	noot	mies
2	Jan 1980	1	−9999.99	1	1-1	1	−9999.99	1
3	Feb 1980	2.3	12.436	2	2-1	2.3	12.436	2
4	Mar 1980	9	13.786	3	3-1	9	13.786	3
5	Apr 1980	4.125	9.456	4	4-1	4.125	9.456	4

In the second example the dates are valid, but column labels (that is, variable names) are missing. Also note that any non-numeric fields are converted to missing values.

	A	B	C	D		GiveWin database		
1	1980-1	1	−9999.99	1		Svar1	Svar2	Svar3
2	1981-1	2.3		2	1980-1	1	−9999.99	1
3	1982-1	9	13.786	3	1981-1	2.3	−9999.99	2
4	1983-1	4.125	9.456	4	1982-1	9	13.786	3
					1983-1	4.125	9.456	4

Finally, both dates and column labels are missing:

	A	B	C		GiveWin database		
1	1	−9999.99	1		Svar1	Svar2	Svar3
2	2.3	12.436	2	1-1	1	−9999.99	1
3	9	13.786	3	2-1	2.3	12.436	2
4	4.125	9.456	4	3-1	9	13.786	3
				4-1	4.125	9.456	4

8.3 Data by variable and data by observation (.DAT)

As the name suggests, a human-readable (or ASCII) data file is a file that can be read using a file viewer or editor. (A binary file cannot be read in this way.) Initial input of data to GiveWin is often in this form, and then saved in the GiveWin format (see §8.1). The default extension is .DAT.

In these two formats, there is no information on sample size, data frequency and variable names. Such information will be prompted when loading the file.

Each variable must have the same number of observations. Variables that have too short a sample have to be padded by missing values (−9999.99). Text following ; or // up to the end of the line is considered to be comment, and skipped. Data files can be ordered by observation (first observation on all variables, second observation on all variables, etc.) or by variable (all observations of first variable, all observations of second variable, and so on). Examples are:

```
// by variable          //by observation
// cons                 891 2.8 //1953 (1)
883 884 885             883 2.7 //1953 (2)
889 891 900             884 3.5 // etc.
// inflat               891 2.8
2.7 3.5 3.9             885 3.9
2.6 2.8 3.4             889 2.6
                        891 2.8
```

GiveWin has additional flexibility in reading human-readable files, by giving the option to treat offending words as missing values, or to skip them. The former can be used to read files with a . or a word for missing values, the latter for comma-separated files. Treating offending words or symbols as missing values can be visualized as:

```
10 M 30                 10 −9999.99 30
                read as →
20 .  40                20 −9999.99 40
```

And for a comma separated example using the skip option:

```
10,5,30,                10 5 30
                read as →
20,6,40,                20 6 40
```

8.4 Data with load info (.DAT)

This data type can be read without intervention, unlike data by observation/variable, which is unstructured. An example is:

```
>CONS 1953 1 1954 1 4

    890.449584960938    886.543029785156    886.328796386719
    884.884704589844    885.254089355469

>INC 1953 1 1954 1 4

    908.212280273438    900.678527832031    899.795288085938
    898.481506347656    895.776916503906
```

The variable description starts with a >, followed by the variable name (no spaces are allowed), the sample and finally the frequency. This is similar to the description in the .IN7 file. The description is followed by the actual data (so the data are always ordered by variable here). As before, text following ; or // up to the end of the line is considered to be comment, and skipped.

8.5 Gauss data file (.DHT/.DAT)

The .DHT/.DAT combination is a format written by Gauss. The .DHT part specifies the size of the data. The .DAT file holds the actual data in binary form. GiveWin can read both 16 and 32 bit .DHT files, but only reads the .DAT file if it holds 8 byte doubles. There is no sample information in the .DHT file, the frequency will be set to one, and the first observation will be at 'year' 1.

GiveWin cannot write .DHT/.DAT files.

8.6 Results file (.OUT)

The contents of text windows are written to the results file, using the default extension .OUT.

8.7 Batch file (.FL)

The batch file stores a set of batch commands, and has the .FL extension. It is a normal text file. The batch language is explained in Chapter 9.

8.8 Algebra file (.ALG)

An algebra file holds the algebra code, and will normally have the .ALG extension. It is a text file and can be edited. The algebra syntax is explained in Chapter 9.

8.9 Matrix file (.MAT)

A matrix file holds a matrix, preceded by two integers which specify the matrix dimensions (number of rows and columns). It will normally have the .MAT extension. Lines starting with ; or // are treated as comments. An example of a matrix file is:

```
2 3         //<-- dimensions, a 2 by 3 matrix
//comment   //<-- a line of comment
1 0 0       //<-- first row of the matrix
0 1 .5      //<-- second row of the matrix
```

8.10 GiveWin graphics file (.GWG)

This is the only graphics storage which can be read back into GiveWin. The file is ASCII, but direct editing will rarely be necessary because all graphics objects can be manipulated on screen. Figure 8.1 corresponds to the following .GWG file:

```
GiveWin 9 1 1
xvec(0,2)
{
 "CONS" 8
 < 890.4495849609375 886.5430297851563 886.3287963867188
   884.8847045898438 885.2540893554688 884.528076171875
   884.4362182617188 884.3106079101563
   >
 "" 0
 1953.75 0.25;
 freq:4;
 symbol:1 4 160;
}
xvec(0,3)
{
 "INC" 8
 < 908.2122802734375 900.6785278320313 899.7952880859375
   898.4815063476563 895.7769165039063 894.830810546875
   892.7406005859375 892.7684936523438
   >
 "" 0
 1953.75 0.25;
 freq:4;
}
axis(0,1)
{
 x;
 label:300 1000 60;
 grid:0 8 1;
 set:0 1 0 0 0 0 0;
}
axis(0,1)
{
 y;
 label:300 1000 60;
 grid:0 8 1;
 set:0 1 0 0 0 0 0;
}
area(0,0)
{
}
legend(0,1)
{
 424 41 0;
 set:300 1 2 1;
```

```
}
line(0,11)
{
 wset:1954.8943148688 904.682339449541
      1954.50327988338 884.077408256881 0;
}
```

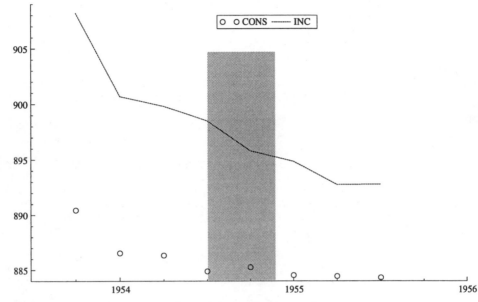

Figure 8.1   A simple graph.

8.11 PostScript file (.EPS)

A PostScript file is an ASCII file which can be printed on any PostScript compat-
ible printer, or on other printers using GhostScript. GhostScript (and its companion,
GhostView for viewing files) can be obtained from the internet.

Direct printing can be achieved simply by copying the file to the PostScript printer.
However, since the file is Encapsulated PostScript (EPS), it will not be centred on the
page. Most popular word-processors can load EPS files.

Figure 8.1 corresponds to the following .EPS file (part is deleted from the listing):

```
%!PS-Adobe-2.0 EPSF-2.0
%%BoundingBox: 0 0 432 288
%%Creator: Ox (C) J.A. Doornik, 1994-1995.
%%Pages: 0
%%EndComments
```

```
%functions
/X     0 def
/Y     0 def
/Rot 0 def
/Slt       { Ltp 0 setdash Lwd setlinewidth } def
/Solid     { [ ] 0 setdash Lwd setlinewidth } def
/Mto       { /Y exch def /X exch def } def
/Lto       { gsave dup 3 -1 roll dup 4 -1 roll newpath X Y
             moveto lineto stroke exch Mto grestore } def
/mt        { moveto } def
/lt        { lineto } def
/BgnPath   { gsave newpath } def
/EndPath   { stroke grestore} def
/Width     { /H exch def /W exch def } def
/SymBox    { newpath X Y moveto X W add Y lineto X W add Y H add
             lineto X Y H add lineto X Y lineto closepath }
             bind def
/SymPlus   { newpath X Y H 2 div add moveto X W add Y H 2 div add
             lineto X W 2 div add Y moveto X W 2 div add Y H add
             lineto closepath } bind def
/SymCirc   { newpath X W 2 div add Y W 2 div add W 2 div 0 360
             arc closepath } bind def
/FillBox   { gsave Width SymBox fill grestore } def
/Box       { gsave Width SymBox Solid stroke grestore } def
/Plus      { gsave Width SymPlus Solid stroke grestore } def
/Circle    { gsave Width SymCirc Solid stroke grestore } def
/Text      { gsave X Y moveto
             Rot 360 eq {dup stringwidth pop neg 0 rmoveto}
             {Rot rotate } ifelse
             show grestore
           } def

%lines
/Linetype0 [ ] def  /Linewidth0 10 def
/Linetype1 [ ] def  /Linewidth1 6 def
/Linetype2 [ ] def  /Linewidth2 10 def
/Linetype3 [50 20] def  /Linewidth3 10 def
/Linetype4 [ ] def  /Linewidth4 10 def
/Linetype5 [35 35] def  /Linewidth5 10 def
/Linetype6 [35 35] def  /Linewidth6 10 def
/Linetype7 [160 80] def  /Linewidth7 10 def
/Linetype8 [160 80] def  /Linewidth8 10 def
/Linetype9 [35 35] def  /Linewidth9 10 def
/Linetype10 [35 35] def  /Linewidth10 10 def
/Linetype11 [ ] def  /Linewidth11 10 def
/Linetype12 [ ] def  /Linewidth12 10 def
/Linetype13 [ ] def  /Linewidth13 10 def
/Linetype14 [ ] def  /Linewidth14 10 def
/Linetype15 [ ] def  /Linewidth15 10 def

%fonts
/Font0     { /Times-Roman findfont exch scalefont setfont } def
/Font1     { /Symbol findfont exch scalefont setfont } def
```

```
/Font2    { /Times-Bold findfont exch scalefont setfont } def
/Font3    { /Times-Italic findfont exch scalefont setfont } def

%colors
/BWG  16 array def
/Gray 16 array def
/RGB  16 array def
% first set all to black
0 1 15 { dup Gray exch 0 put RGB exch [0 0 0] put } for

% color 0: white <-- background colour
% color 1: black <-- foreground colour
BWG  0 0.00 put   Gray  0 1.00 put   RGB  0 [1.00 1.00 1.00] put
BWG  1 0.00 put   Gray  1 0.00 put   RGB  1 [0.00 0.00 0.00] put
BWG  2 0.00 put   Gray  2 0.30 put   RGB  2 [1.00 0.00 0.00] put
BWG  3 0.00 put   Gray  3 0.11 put   RGB  3 [0.00 0.00 1.00] put
BWG  4 0.00 put   Gray  4 0.35 put   RGB  4 [0.00 0.50 0.50] put
BWG  5 0.00 put   Gray  5 0.41 put   RGB  5 [1.00 0.00 1.00] put
BWG  6 0.00 put   Gray  6 0.44 put   RGB  6 [0.00 0.75 0.00] put
BWG  7 0.00 put   Gray  7 0.45 put   RGB  7 [0.50 0.50 0.00] put
BWG  8 0.00 put   Gray  8 0.21 put   RGB  8 [0.50 0.00 0.50] put
BWG  9 0.95 put   Gray  9 0.95 put   RGB  9 [1.00 1.00 0.50] put
BWG 10 0.80 put   Gray 10 0.80 put   RGB 10 [0.50 0.50 0.50] put
BWG 11 0.85 put   Gray 11 0.85 put   RGB 11 [0.50 1.00 1.00] put
BWG 12 0.70 put   Gray 12 0.70 put   RGB 12 [0.00 1.00 1.00] put
BWG 13 0.25 put   Gray 13 0.25 put   RGB 13 [0.25 0.25 0.25] put
BWG 14 0.50 put   Gray 14 0.50 put   RGB 14 [0.50 0.50 0.50] put
BWG 15 0.75 put   Gray 15 0.75 put   RGB 15 [0.75 0.75 0.75] put

%choose a ColorModel:
% 0=black/white; 1=black/white/gray; 2=gray; 3=color
/ColorModel 1 def

/SetColor
  { ColorModel 0 eq
     { 0 eq {1 setgray}{0 setgray} ifelse }
     { ColorModel 1 eq
        { BWG exch get setgray}
        { ColorModel 2 eq
           { Gray exch get setgray}
           { RGB exch get aload pop setrgbcolor} ifelse
        } ifelse
     } ifelse
} def

%init
save
280 Font0
10 setlinewidth
/Ltp Linetype1 def
/Lwd Linewidth1 def
```

```
0.0288 0.0288 scale
%0.0500 0.0500 scale 11000 900 translate 90 rotate

%Graph start
11 SetColor
/Ltp { Linetype11 } def /Lwd { Linewidth11 } def Slt
6145 667 Mto
2146 7186 FillBox
6145 667 Mto
2 SetColor
/Ltp { Linetype2 } def /Lwd { Linewidth2 } def Slt
1932 2809 Mto
160 160 Circle
3304 1447 Mto
160 160 Circle
4676 1372 Mto
160 160 Circle
6048 868 Mto
160 160 Circle
7420 997 Mto
160 160 Circle
8792 744 Mto
160 160 Circle
10164 712 Mto
160 160 Circle
11536 668 Mto
160 160 Circle
11536 668 Mto
3 SetColor
/Ltp { Linetype3 } def /Lwd { Linewidth3 } def Slt
BgnPath
2012 9085 mt
3384 6457 lt
4756 6149 lt
6128 5691 lt
7500 4747 lt
8872 4417 lt
10244 3688 lt
11616 3698 lt
EndPath
1 SetColor
/Ltp { Linetype1 } def /Lwd { Linewidth1 } def Slt
3384 640 Mto
3384 700 Lto
%%              rest of line deleted
/Rot 0 def
300 Font0
3100 280 Mto
(1954) Text
8588 280 Mto
(1955) Text
14076 280 Mto
(1956) Text
```

```
1 SetColor
/Ltp { Linetype1 } def /Lwd { Linewidth1 } def Slt
640 988 Mto
700 988 Lto
%%                    rest of line deleted
/Rot 360 def
300 Font0
546 875 Mto
(885) Text
546 2619 Mto
(890) Text
546 4363 Mto
(895) Text
546 6107 Mto
(900) Text
546 7851 Mto
(905) Text
/Rot 0 def
/Rot 0 def
2 SetColor
/Ltp { Linetype2 } def /Lwd { Linewidth2 } def Slt
6556 8713 Mto
160 160 Circle
6997 8713 Mto
160 160 Circle
6997 8713 Mto
1 SetColor
300 Font0
7257 8703 Mto
(CONS) Text
3 SetColor
/Ltp { Linetype3 } def /Lwd { Linewidth3 } def Slt
BgnPath
8197 8793 mt
8796 8793 lt
EndPath
1 SetColor
300 Font0
8897 8703 Mto
(INC) Text
6457 8583 Mto
1 SetColor
/Ltp { Linetype1 } def /Lwd { Linewidth1 } def Slt
3170 420 Box
6457 8583 Mto
%Graph end

restore
showpage
%%EOF
```

Sometimes minor changes need be made after saving the file, e.g.:

- Changing colour model.

   0 Black and white

   All non-white colours are translated to black.

   1 Black, white, gray

   Colour 0 is white, colours 1–8 are black, the remainder are translated to a grey value. One additional change to the line types is made: if line 2 and 3 are both solid, line 3 is changed to a dotted line.

   2 Gray levels

   Colour 0 is white, colours 1 is black, the remainder are translated to a grey value.

   3 Color

   Will result in a colour graph on a colour printer, else the result will be translated to grey levels inside the printer.

   The statement /ColorModel 1 def sets the colour model.

   The PostScript Setup command on the Tools menu allows choosing a colour model to be used when saving the file.

- Changing line types. For example, to make line two twice as thick, and dashed, change

```
/Linetype2 [ ] def  /Linewidth2 10 def
```

   to

```
/Linetype2 [40 40] def  /Linewidth2 20 def
```

   The [40 40] defines the pattern: 40 units line, followed by a gap of 40 units. Note that line type 1 is the black line, used for axes. Line type two is the one used for the first vector. Line type 0 is usually invisible (white line on white background)

- Changing font sizes. Whenever a font is chosen, it is preceded by the font size, as in:

```
300 Font0
```

   which selects font 0 (set to Times-Roman) at size 300.

- Full page print.

   As was pointed out before, when copying the EPS file to the printer, it will not fill the page. To print the graph in landscape filling a full A4 page, change

```
0.0288 0.0288 scale
%0.0500 0.0500 scale 11000 900 translate 90 rotate
```

   to

```
%0.0288 0.0288 scale
0.0500 0.0500 scale 11000 900 translate 90 rotate
```

When loading the EPS file into a word-processor, that program will be able to resize the graph to any desired size.

8.12 Windows meta file (.WMF)

A WMF file is a binary file which stores the Windows commands which are used when displaying the graph on screen. Since the graphs are drawn in vector form, the WMF will be a vector graph. WMF files can be read by many programs, and edited further.

Note It seems that the WMF files written by GiveWin cannot readily be read into Microsoft Word. At the moment of writing, we have not solved this problem. Copying and pasting graphs (which also uses .WMF format) from GiveWin into Word works without problems. Scientific Word can read GiveWin WMF files from disk or from the clipboard.

8.13 Enhanced meta file (.EMF)

The EMF format is a more recent version of WMF file, and can only be created in Windows NT and Windows 95.

Chapter 9

GiveWin Languages

GiveWin is mostly menu-driven for ease of use. To add flexibility, certain functions can be accessed through entering commands. The syntax of these commands, which can be seen as little computer languages, is described in this chapter. In addition, there is Ox, which is a more serious computer language, and described in a separate book.

9.1 Calculator (Alt+c)

The calculator enables easy manipulation of the variables in the database, and is a convenient way to write algebra expressions.

The aim is to build a valid algebra expression in the expression window (without the assignment part and the terminating semi-colon). All successful transformations are logged in the Results window.

9.2 Algebra (Alt+a)

The Algebra command enables you to transform the database variables by typing mathematical formulae into an editor. The algebra code can be saved and reloaded. The algebra syntax in GiveWin has some minor changes from PcGive version 8. These changes mainly consist of name changes of a few functions for compatibility with Ox, and the addition of some new functions.

Algebra is a simple vector language, operating on only one type of object: the variables in the database. This object is manipulated as a whole, although it is possible to limit access to a subsample. The only valid statements are assignments and conditional assignments. Statements have to be terminated with a semicolon.

If an error occurs while executing the algebra code, the processing will be aborted, and control returned to GiveWin. All successful statements up to that point will have been executed, with corresponding changes to the database. Take this into account when rerunning the corrected code.

9.2.1 Variables and variable names

Names are made up of letters and digits. The first character must be a letter. Underscores (_) count as a letter. Valid names are CONS, cons, cons_1, _a_1_b, etc. Examples of invalid names are ΔCONS, 1-CONS, log(X), etc. Invalid names may be used in Algebra when enclosed in double quotes, so

```
"log(X)" = log(X);
```

is valid as long as the variable called X exists. Algebra is case-sensitive: CONS and cons refer to different variables. When you create a new variable through an assignment operation, it is immediately added to the database, and initialized to missing values. If necessary the database name will be truncated (longer names are allowed in algebra than in the database).

9.2.2 Comment

Anything between /* and */ is considered comment. Note that this comment cannot be nested. So

```
aap = CONS + 1; /* comment /* nested comment */ */
```

leads to a syntax error. Everything following // up to the end of the line is also comment.

9.2.3 Constants

A constant is a number which is used in an expression. Examples are 1, 1.2, .5, −77000, −.5e−10 and 2.1E−12.

9.2.4 Arithmetic operators

The binary arithmetic operators are ^, *, /, +, −. The ^ is the power operator; CONS ^2 raises the variable CONS to the power two. All computations are double precision floating point arithmetic. The precedence order is unary +, −, then ^, then *, /, and finally +, −. An example of unary minus is: $x = −1$. Any arithmetic operation involving missing values returns a missing value.

9.2.5 Relational and logical operators

The relational operators are <, <=, >, >=, standing for 'less', 'less or equal', 'greater', 'greater or equal'. The equality operators are == and !=, 'is equal to' and is 'not equal to'. These are ranked below the relational operators in precedence. Ranked yet lower are logical AND (&&) and logical OR (||). The unary negation operator ! has the highest precedence. An example of unary negation is:

```
new = !season();
```

new will have a 0 where the season function returns a 1, and vice versa. Boolean arithmetic is also done in floating point. The numeric result is 1. for an expression that evaluates to true, and 0. for one that is false. An expression with value 0 is false, with value not 0 is true. There is no special treatment of missing values in a logical operation. Note that | is the ASCII 124 symbol.

9.2.6 Assignment statements

The assignment operator is the = symbol. Assignment statements have to be terminated by a semicolon (;). If the variable to which a result is assigned does not yet exist, it is created and added to the database. Otherwise the existing variable is overwritten. Note that assignment expressions are vector expressions: all observations will be overwritten (it is possible to restrict assignment to a subsample using the insample function). Some valid assignment statements are:

```
cons2 = 2 * CONS - 1;
cons3 = CONS / 3 - (cons2 + 5) * 1.55;
Seasonal = season();
```

The last statement constructs a variable called Seasonal, which is 1 in period 1, and 0 otherwise. This variable will be used in further examples.

Don't confuse = and == ; = assigns, while == compares. Parentheses may be used in expressions in the usual way; in the example above (cons2 + 5) * 1.55 evaluates to cons2 * 1.55 + 5 * 1.55.

9.2.7 Conditional assignment statements

The conditional assignment expression has the following form:

TestExpression ? *TrueExpression* : *FalseExpression*

First the *TestExpression* is evaluated; if it is true (not 0.), then *TrueExpression* will be evaluated, else *FalseExpression*. Let us consider an example involving the Seasonal variable created above, which is 1 in the first quarter, and 0 in the other quarters. The statement

```
new = Seasonal ? CONS : 0;
```

can be read as follows: the variable new will get the value of CONS when Seasonal is true (that is, when Seasonal is not 0., so in the first quarter of each year), else it will get the value 0. In this case, the same result could have been reached with:

```
new = Seasonal * CONS;
```

However, if we had used a seasonal with the value 2 in the first quarter, and the rest zeros, then only the conditional assignment would have given the desired result (since 2 is not false, and hence true).

Note that the ': *FalseExpression*' part is optional. For example:

```
new = Seasonal ? CONS;
```

is a valid conditional assignment statement. Now the variable will have the value of CONS for the first quarter, but the other observations of new are not touched (so if new is created by this expression, it will contain missing values for quarters 2, 3 and 4, making the variable unusable for modelling purposes). Another example:

```
new = (CONS == MISSING) ? 0 : CONS;
```

This new variable takes the values of CONS, replacing missing values by zeros.

9.2.8 Keywords

The following keywords are reserved by algebra:

FALSE	0.
TRUE	!FALSE
FREQUENCY	data frequency
MISSING	the missing value
PI	Pi (3.1415..)
NOBS	number of observations

9.2.9 Functions

A large set of functions is provided by algebra. Most of these take both variables and constants as arguments. A function name must be followed by parentheses, even if it doesn't take any arguments. See the algebra function list of Table 9.1 for function definitions. Some examples of statements involving functions are:

```
lcons = log (CONS);      // takes the natural logarithm of CONS
cons_1 = lag(CONS, 1);                      // lag CONS one period
ccons = exp(log(CONS));              // gives back original CONS

dummy = insample(1979, 1, 1983, 4) ? log(cons) : 0;
             // Dummy will be log(cons) for the period 1979(1)
             // to 1983(4), and 0 outside it.

trough = (lag(trough,1) == MISSING || CONS < lag(trough,1))
       ? CONS : lag(trough,1);
                         // Try to understand this statement;
             // a trough can be created with the Calculator too.

dummy  = (year() == 1979) ? 1 : 0;  // creates a dummy variable
```

9.2.10 Sorting functions

The sort functions change the order of observations in the database and must be handled with care. Note that the trend() function can be used to create a variable which corresponds to the original observation index of the data. So if that variable is sorted together with the variable we wish to sort, it can be used to 'unsort' the variable.

_sortby($arg1$, $arg2$)

Sorts the variable $arg1$ in increasing order, and sorts $arg2$ accordingly. Returns the value of $arg1$ after sorting. Both $arg1$ and $arg2$ must be variables. Suppose the residuals of a regression have been saved in the variable called Residual, then a sorted residual is created as follows:

```
index = trend();
tmp = _sortby(Residual, index);
                /* Residual is sorted, and index accordingly */
                              /* tmp is a dummy variable, */
                    /* at this stage identical to Residual. */
            /* Now it is easy to locate outliers in Residual */
```

The following statement will reset the old ordering (do not rerun the index = trend(); statement, because that will overwrite the index and lose the information on the original ordering):

```
tmp = _sortby(index, Residual);
                        /* Restores index and Residual, */
                /* at this stage index is equal to Trend. */
```

_sortallby($arg1$)

Sorts the variable $arg1$ in increasing order, and sorts the whole database accordingly. Returns the value of $arg1$ after sorting. This function will be most useful with cross-section data; for example, to push missing values to the end:

```
exclude =
    (Var1 == MISSING || Var2 == MISSING || Var3 == MISSING);
    /* exclude is 1 for each observation where any of the
            three variables has a missing value, 0 elsewhere */

tmp = _sortallby(exclude);
            /* the observations without any missing values will
                precede those with missing values, making it easy
                            to exclude them from the regression.
                The Trend can be used to restore the order */
```

9.2.11 Smoothing functions

The smoothing functions which are available in cross plots can also be accessed from algebra. Chapter 7 briefly reviews the mathematics underlying the smoothers.

9.2.11.1 Hodrick–Prescott filter

The Hodrick–Prescott is a filter which is popular in macro-economics, and virtually identical to a natural cubic spline with bandwidth 1600. The syntax is:

$$var\_dest = \text{smooth\_hp}(var, alpha, var\_dest);$$

where *var* is the variable to be smoothed, *alpha* is the bandwith (use 0 for the default of 1600), and *var_dest* is the destination variable (must be different from *var*). For example:

```
hpCONS = smooth_hp(CONS, 0, hpCONS);
```

which creates hpCONS through the assignment statement, and uses it as the destination for the fitted values from the filter.

If there are missing values in the data series, smooth_hp uses data starting from the first valid observation, and stopping at the first missing value thereafter. The sample used can be restricted using the insample function.

9.2.11.2 Kernel and spline smoothing

The kernel based smoother (using the Epanechnikov kernel), and the natural cubic spline are computed respectively by:

$$var\_dest = \text{smooth\_np}(var, alpha, var\_dest);$$
$$var\_dest = \text{smooth\_sp}(var, alpha, var\_dest);$$

where *var* is the variable to be smoothed, *var_dest* is the destination variable (must be different from *var*), and *alpha* is the bandwith, used as follows:

   0 use automatic bandwidth selection based on generalized cross validation;

  < 0 the absolute value is used for the bandwidth;

  > 0 specifies the equivalent number of parameters to be used.

These functions will use all available observations (unless restricted by the insample function), and will fill in missing values using the fit from the smoother.

Some examples are:

```
sp1CONS = smooth_sp(CONS,     0, sp1CONS);
sp3CONS = smooth_sp(CONS,    10, sp3CONS);
sp2CONS = smooth_sp(CONS, -1600, sp2CONS);
```

The first uses automatic bandwidth selection, the second sets the bandwidth implicitly by specifying an equivalent number of parameters, and the last line sets the bandwidth directly to 1600.

9.2.12 Algebra function list

Available functions are listed in Table 9.1. Any function operating on missing values returns a missing value (-9999.99). Any function which fails also returns a missing value. Where the argument is *var*, it must be just a variable name, e.g. one = 1; cum(one); is allowed, but cum(1) is not. The mathematics of several functions is presented in Table 9.2. Some examples were given in §9.1; for additional advanced examples using algebra: see Chapter 6.

NOTE Some functions have been renamed for consistency with Ox: ran, rannormal and tailnormal are now called ranu, rann and tailn respectively.

Table 9.1   Algebra functions.

Function	Returns
acos(*arg*)	arccosine of *arg*, or 0 if $|arg| > 1$
almon(*var,arg,power*)	almon lag of *var*
asin(*arg*)	arcsine of *arg*, or 0 if $|arg| > 1$
atan(*arg*)	arctangent of *arg*
ceil(*arg*)	ceiling of *arg* (the smallest integer $\geq arg$)
cos(*arg*)	cosine of *arg*
cum(*var*)	cumulative sum of *var*
denschi(*arg*)	$\chi^2(arg)$ density
densf(*arg1,arg2*)	F(*arg1, arg2*) density
densn()	N(0, 1) density
denst(*arg1*)	student-t(*arg*) density
diff(*var,arg*)	arg^{th} difference of *var*, or the missing value if *var* is not a variable, or the difference cannot be taken
div(*arg1,arg2*)	returns the result of the (32 bit) integer division
dummy(*yr1,per1,yr2,per2*)	1 inside the sample *yr1 (per1) yr2 (per2)*, 0 outside it
exp(*arg*)	exponential function of *arg*
fabs(*arg*)	absolute value of *arg*
floor(*arg*)	floor of *arg* (the smallest integer $\leq arg$)
fmod(*arg1,arg2*)	floating point remainder of *arg1/arg2*
insample(*yr1,per1,yr2,per2*)	true if inside the sample *yr1(per1)* to *yr2(per2)*, false outside
lag(*var,arg*)	arg^{th} lag of *var*, or the missing value if *arg1* is not a variable, or the lag cannot be taken
log(*arg*)	natural logarithm of *arg*
log10(*arg*)	base-10 logarithm of *arg*
loggamma(*arg*)	logarithm of the gamma function at *arg*
max(*arg1, arg2*)	maximum of *arg1* and *arg2*
mean(*var*)	mean of *var*
min(*arg1,arg2*)	minimum of *arg1* and *arg2*
movingavg(*var,lag,lead*)	the moving average of *var*
movingSD(*var,lag,lead,mvar*)	the moving standard deviation of *var* around *mvar*
period()	current period
probn(*arg1*)	$P(X \leq arg1 | X \sim N(0, 1))$
quanchi(*p,arg*)	$\chi^2(arg)$ quantiles at *p*
quanf(*p,arg1,arg2*)	F(*arg1, arg2*) quantiles at *arg1*
quann(*p*)	N(0, 1) quantiles at *p*
quant(*p,arg1*)	student-t(*arg*) quantiles at *p*

Function	Returns	(Continued)
ranu()	uniform random numbers	
ranchi(*arg*)	$\chi^2(arg)$ random numbers	
ranf(*arg1,arg2*)	F(*arg1, arg2*) random numbers	
rann()	N(0, 1) random numbers	
rant(*arg1*)	student-t(*arg*) random numbers	
ranseed(*arg*)	sets the random number seed to *arg*, returns *arg*	
round(*arg*)	rounded value of *arg*	
season()	1 in period 1, 0 otherwise	
sin(*arg*)	sine of *arg*	
smooth_hp(*var,alpha,dest*)	see §9.2.11	
smooth_np(*var,alpha,dest*)	see §9.2.11	
smooth_sp(*var,alpha,dest*)	see §9.2.11	
sort(*var*)	see §9.2.10	
_sortby(*var1, var2*)	see §9.2.10	
_sortallby(*var1*)	see §9.2.10	
sqrt(*arg*)	square root of *arg*	
stock(*var,arvalue,init*)	integrates *var*	
stockv(*var,arvar,init*)	integrates *var*	
tailchi(*arg1,arg2*)	$P(X \geq arg1 \vert X \sim \chi^2(arg2))$	
tailf(*arg1,arg2,arg3*)	$P(X \geq arg1 \vert X \sim$ F$(arg2, arg3))$	
tailn(*arg1*)	$P(X \geq arg1 \vert X \sim$ N$(0, 1))$	
tailt(*arg1,arg2*)	$P(X \geq arg1 \vert X \sim$ t$(arg2))$	
tan(*arg*)	tangent of *arg*	
trend()	1 for the first observation, 2 for the second, etc.	
variance(*var*)	variance of *var*	
year()	current year.	

Table 9.2   Mathematics of some Algebra functions.

Function	Result
lag(x, c)	x_{t-c}, $c > 0$ or $c < 0$
diff(x, c)	$x_t - x_{t-c}$, $c > 0$
almon(x, c_1, c_2)	$\sum_{k=0}^{c_1}(c_1 + 1 - i)^{c_2} x_{t-i} / \sum_{k=0}^{c_1}(c_1 + 1 - i)^{c_2}$
movingavg(x, c_1, c_2)	$\sum_{k=t-c_1}^{t+c_2} x_k / (c_2 + c_1 + 1)$
movingSD(x, c_1, c_2, z)	$\left[\sum_{k=t-c_1}^{t+c_2} (x_k - z_k)^2 / (c_2 + c_1 + 1) \right]^{1/2}$
stock(x, c_1, c_2)	$(1 - c_1)y_{t-1} + x_t$, given $y_0 = c_2$
stockv(x, z, c_2)	$(1 - z_t)y_{t-1} + x_t$, given $y_0 = c_2$

9.2.13 Algebra operator precedence

Table 9.3 lists the operator precedence, with the highest precedence at the top of the table.

Table 9.3   Algebra operator precedence.

Symbol	Description	Associativity
!	Logical NOT	Right to left
–	Unary minus	
+	Unary plus	
^	Power	Left to right
*	Multiply	Left to right
/	Divide	
+	Add	Left to right
–	Subtract	
<	Less than	Left to right
<=	Less than or equal to	
>	Greater than	
>–	Greater than or equal to	
==	Equal	Left to right
!=	Not equal	
&&	Logical AND	Left to right
||	Logical OR	Left to right

9.3 Batch (Alt+b)

This section gives an alphabetical list of the GiveWin batch language statements. There are two types: function calls (with or without arguments) terminated by a semicolon, and commands, which are followed by statements between curly brackets. Other programs (such as PcGive, PcFiml, STAMP) extend this batch language with their own module-specific commands.

Anything between /* and */ is considered comment. Note that this comment cannot be nested. Everything following // up to the end of the line is also comment.

GiveWin allows you to save the most recent model from the current module as a batch file. If a model has been created interactively, it can be saved as a batch file for

Table 9.4   Batch language syntax summary.

algebra { ... }
appenddata(*"filename"* , *"group"*);
appresults(*"filename"*);
break;
database(*year1, period1, year2, period2, frequency*);
exit;
loaddata(*"filename"*);
module(*"name"*);
savedata(*"filename"*);
saveresults(*"filename"*);
usedata(*"databasename"*);

further editing or easy recall in a later session. This is also the most convenient way to create a batch file.

If an error occurs during processing, the batch run will be aborted and control returned to GiveWin.

In the following list, function arguments are indicated by *words*, whereas the areas where statement blocks are expected are indicated by .... Examples follow the list of descriptions. For terms in double quotes, the desired term must be substituted and provided together with the quotes. A command summary is given in Table 9.4. Module specific commands are documented with each module.

algebra { ... }
> Contains the algebra code to execute.

appenddata(*"filename"* , *"group"*);
> Append the data from the named .IN7 file to the existing in-memory database. If the database does not yet exist it must be created first using the database() function. If the second argument is " " (that is, no group name is specified) the whole file will be appended, otherwise just the named group.

appresults(*"filename"*);
> Append the contents of the Results window to the named file and *clear the Results window*. This command could be useful in very long batch files, to prevent the Results window from filling up.

break;
> Stop the batch file, return to GiveWin menus. While a batch file is running, there is no way of stopping it other than this inbuilt command.

exit;
> Exits GiveWin.

loaddata(*"filename"*);
> Load the data from the named .IN7 file. To load, a full pathname would normally have to be specified, e.g. `"c:\mydata\data.in7"`. The extension indicates

the data type and must be provided. Inside GiveWin, the database will then be known as data.in7, and will be the current default database.

module(*"name"*);

>   Starts the specified module. When the module is already active, it becomes the focus for subsequent module-specific batch commands. Otherwise the module is started first.
>
>   **NOTE:** In our experience, the 'hand-shake' between the module and GiveWin does not always work when the module is not active yet. The problem appears to arise when other programs are taking up a lot of computer resources, in which case the communication link is not established in time.

savedata(*"filename"*);

>   Save the current database to the named .IN7 file. The .BN7 file will get the same base name. If files with these names already exist, they will be overwritten!

saveresults(*"filename"*);

>   Save the contents of the results to the named file and *clear the Results window*. If a file with that name already exists, it will be overwritten!

usedata(*"databasename"*);

>   Sets the default database to *databasename*. The database must already be loaded into GiveWin.

We finish with an annotated example using all commands, and also some commands from the PcGive module.

```
database("test", 1950, 1, 2000, 4, 4);  // Create the database
                          // Append the tutorial data set to test
           // note that test has a longer sample then data.in7
appenddata("c:\givewin\data.in7", "");
loaddata("c:\givewin\data.in7"); // Load the tutorial data. We
  // now have two databases, with data.in7 the default database
usedata("test");             // make test the default database

algebra
{                           // Create SAVINGSL in database test
    SAVINGSL = lag(INC,1) - lag(CONS, 1);
}
module("PcGive");
system
{
    Y = CONS;                      // The endogenous variable
    Z = Constant, CONS_1, CONS_2;           // the regressors
}
estsystem("OLS", 1953, 3, 1992, 3, 8, 0, 0);
              // Estimate the system by OLS over 1953(2)-1992(3)
              // withhold 8 forecasts, use 0 for initialization
                      // the last 0 is only relevant in PcFiml
saveresults("TEST");        // Save the contents of the Results
                      // window to TEST.OUT and clear the window
testsummary;                           // Do the test summary
```

```
appresults("TEST");        // Append the contents of the Results
                           // window to TEST.OUT, and clear the window

break;                              // stop the batch run, remaining
                                    // commands will not be ·executed
savedata("NEWTEST");    // save test to NEWTEST.IN7/NEWTEST.BN7
exit;                                           // Exit GiveWin
```

Chapter 10

GiveWin graphics

10.1 Graphics paper

Graphs in GiveWin are drawn on a graphics worksheet, consisting of 10 000 by 15 000 pixels, with (0,0) in the bottom left corner:

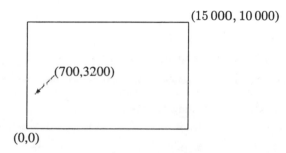

These pixels are virtual and different from screen pixels: the paper is always 10 000 × 15 000, regardless of the screen resolution or the size on screen.

Positions can be specified in pixel coordinates, as for example $(p_x, p_y) = (70, 3200)$. More often it is convenient to use real world coordinates to map the pixel coordinates into real data values. This is done by specifying an area on the graphics worksheet, and attaching real world coordinates to it. These areas are allowed to overlap, but need not:

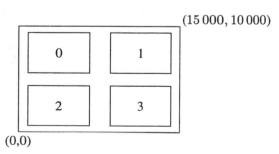

The areas are numbered from left to right and top to bottom, *counting starts at zero.*

Suppose we have set up all areas as being from $(x, y) = (0.0, 0.0)$ to $(x, y) = (1.0, 1.0)$ (again within each area the origin is the lower left corner). Then we can draw a line through area 2 in two ways:

(1) in real coordinates within an area

>   step 1: select area 2;
>   step 2: move to (0.0, 0.0);
>   step 3: draw a line to (1.0,1.0).

(2) using pixel coordinates on the worksheet

>   step 1: move to pixel coordinates (600,600);
>   step 2: draw a line to pixel coordinates (3600, 3600).

where we assume that (600,600) to (3600,3600) are the pixel coordinates chosen for area 2. Drawing in real world coordinates has the advantage that it corresponds more closely to our data.

10.2 Creating graphs

A graph is created from data in a database using the Graphics toolbar button, or Tools/Graphics. These graphs appear in the a window labelled GiveWin Graphics. Subsequent graphs are added to this window. To start from scratch, close the window, or select and delete each area. To keep the existing GiveWin graphics window, use View/Keep graph (note that the menu contents change according to the type of window which is active).

Modules such as PcGive will put their graphs in a window with a different name. The various types of graphs are discussed in Chapter 4.

10.3 Printing graphs

Select File/Print to print to an attached printer. The following control of headers and footers is available for printing from Tools/Page Setup:

- Draw a box around the graph;
- Draw a header for the graph. This is controlled via the Header and Footer boxes. There are four specials:
    - `&[date]` prints the date,
    - `&[time]` prints the time,
    - `&[page]` prints the page number,
    - `&[file]` prints the file name.

Other text in the edit field is printed directly.

- Fit to Page: when selected, the graph will fill the entire page.

The print setup is printer specific. In many cases one of the options is whether to print in landscape or portrait mode.

Use File/Print Preview to view the result before printing. Note that colours will come out in grey levels (unless you have a colour printer of course).

10.4 Graphics formats

Graphics file formats are discussed in §8.10–§8.13.

10.5 Saving and loading graphs

Use File/Save As or the diskette toolbar button to save the graph to a file. At the bottom of the dialog is a dropdown listbox in which you select the type of file.

Only .GWG files can be read back into GiveWin. Note however, that no other program can read such files. Choose File/Open, and select GiveWin graphics for the file type.

10.6 Graphics objects

Each graph consists of a collection of objects, which in most cases can be manipulated, moved or deleted. The main one, the area, was introduced in §10.1.

10.6.1 Area

An area defines a rectangle on the paper which has world coordinates attached to it. The concept of areas enables multiple graphs on the paper, up to 36. Areas are allowed to overlap.

By default, an area has 'automatic' pixel coordinates, which means that, when an area is added the pre-existing area will automatically shrink to make space. An area can be selected with the mouse, and moved around the paper. This changes the automatic paper positioning into a fixed position. Real world coordinates are also selected automatically, but can be set to fixed values.

The Area page of the Graphics Property dialog allows additional adjustments. Activate this dialog through Edit/Edit Graph, or by double clicking in an area. You can:

- change world coordinates: select the desired area and deselect the auto checkbox for the X or Y coordinates, then adjust the settings. Press All to apply this to all areas.
- reset pixel coordinates to automatic or manually adjust pixel coordinates.
- change layout, e.g. for example from 2×1 to 1×2.

10.6.2 Variable and line attributes

The variable (or vector) is the main graphics object: it consists of a sequence of observations, graphed against time or another variable. A variable cannot be moved, nor can
observations be moved on screen. When a variable in a database is graphed, it has a 'hot-
link': if an observation in the database is changed, the vector in the graph will change.

There are essentially three types of vectors:

- variable against time;
- variable against another variable; use Swap on the Line Attributes page of Graphics Properties to swap the X and Y variable;
- variable against another variable by a third variable. The third variable can indicate symbol size, have its value printed, or specify error bars. Use Swap to swap
  the X and Y variable, the Z variable will not be affected.

The Line Attributes page of the Graphics Property dialog controls how the vector
is displayed. The line joining the observations can be

- None: not linked,
- Line: linked,
- Index Line: this draws a line from the point to the zero axis (if part of the area),
  or the edge of the area (towards zero).

The observations can be marked by a symbol, and the size of that symbol can be set.
The colour and type with which lines and symbols are drawn is set in the Color/type field.
It selects one of the 16 line types, which are set in Tools/Graphics Setup (also accessed
through the Setup button in the Graphics Property dialog).

The Regression, Scale page of the Graphics Property dialog allows adding regression lines to variables, and adjustment of the scaling (relative to the selected variable):

- None removes all scaling.
- Means matches the means of all variables to that of the selected variable: the shift
  factor will be set to make the means of the variables equal.
- Ranges: the scale factor will be set to give all the variables the same range. Maximum – minimum will now be the same for every variable. Adjustment is made
  relative to the selected variable.
- Both matches means and ranges. Both the shift and scale factors are set.

The scale and shift factor can also be set directly.

The regression options in this page are:

- Number of least squares lines.
  By default no least squares lines are drawn; you can select up to 40 lines.
- Sequential versus Recursive regression lines.
  The default is sequential regression: the X-axis is divided in s sections (where
  s is the number of regression lines). Each section gets its own regression line.

Recursive regression lines will lead to each subsequent section added on to the previous.

- Projections shows the deviation between the variable and the regression line.
- Line no sets the line type.

10.6.3 Axes

An X and Y axis is added automatically to each graph. Usually the default suffices, but a large number of adjustments can be made in the Axes page of the Graphics Property dialog. Each axis consists of (values are in world coordinates):

- Minimum and maximum;
- First large: the value at which the first large tick mark appears;
- Large Step: the gap between large tick marks;
- Small Step: the gap between small tick marks;
- Anchor: determines where the axis is anchored, e.g. for an X-axis this is a Y value (changing the anchor would move the X-axis up or down). Min anchors at the left (bottom) of an area, Max at the right (top). User allows anchoring anywhere in the graph.

The following adjustments can be made to an axis (all adjustments apply to the current axis only):

- when Automatic is unchecked, any of the above axis properties can be adjusted.
- hide an axis by unchecking Show. (Axes can also be deleted, but when an area has no X or Y axis and is redrawn, that axis will be added.)
- set the anchoring: Min anchors at the left (bottom) of an area, Max at the right (top). User allows anchoring anywhere in the graph.
- The Tick Size. This sets the small tick size, the large tick size is twice the small tick size.
- The Font Size sets the size of the axis labels.
- Grid attaches a grid, perpendicular to the selected axis. The grid is at the large tick marks. The grid colour and type is set in Graphics Setup, the default is that of line colour and type 14.
- No Line removes the line, leaving only tick marks.
- Labels above puts the labels on the other side of the axis.
- Line at 0 is only for X-axes, and uses the same line colour and type as the grid. By default a line showing zero is added when both negative and positive data occur.
- Centre dates puts the labels in between the tick marks. For example for annual data, the label 1960 is centred at 1960 by default. With Centre dates it is set half way between 1960 and 1961. This option is for X axes only.
- No small Y removes the small tickmarks (Y axis only).

Note that you may have as many axes as you wish. Axes cannot be selected or manipulated on screen with the mouse.

10.6.4 Legends

Legends are added automatically in an appropriate size, unless the graph gets too small. In that case (normally with more than six areas), the legend will be hidden. To unhide a legend in a small graph, it is required that both Hide legend and Resize are not marked.

Legends can be selected with the mouse, and moved around. Resizing of the legend box is only possible when Auto box size is not set. The available options in the Legends etc page of the Graphics Property dialog are:

- Hide legend, legends are never completely deleted.
- No columns sets the number of columns for the labels; the default is two.
- Font size determines the size of the label. This is shrunk further when Resize is set.
- Boxed draws a box around the legends.
- Auto box size leaves the box size to GiveWin. If not marked, you can adjust the box size with the mouse.
- Resize allows GiveWin to shrink the legend box as the area gets smaller.
- Apply to all also applies all the above options to the legends of all other areas.

10.6.5 Histogram

Histograms are also controlled through the Legends etc page of the Graphics Property dialog. The only available option is to select a line color/type for the outside line and for the area inside the boxes.

10.6.6 Text

Text can be added from the Edit menu using Add Text. Text belongs to an area, in which case it is deleted if the area is deleted (or copied when the area is copied). Text entered outside any area will be part of area 0. Only one line of text can be entered at a time.

Text entered immediately above the graph will have the title property, which means that it is moved with the area when the area is moved.

It is possible to change the font of the text and the size. Four fonts are predefined:

- Times New Roman
- Symbol
- Times New Roman bold
- Times New Roman italic

Double click on a font in the list in the Layout page of Graphics Setup to change the font definition.

10.6.7 Lines

Lines can be added from the Edit menu using Draw Line. Lines coordinates may be specified in world coordinates (the default when the line is drawn inside an area), in which case the line is deleted if the area is deleted (or copied when the area is copied). Alternatively, lines may be specified in pixel coordinates. The appearance of a line can be changed to a box or a solid box.

The Lines page from the Graphics Setup allows changing the default colour, type and thickness of the line. Note that for Windows 95 and 3.1, user defined lines and dashed lines do not draw properly; also, width for dotted and long-dashed lines does not work.

10.6.8 Adding, moving and deleting objects

Objects are added from the Edit menu. Several objects can be selected with the mouse, and moved and deleted subsequently.

10.6.9 Grid

A grid can be activated from the View menu, to allow objects to be lined up.

10.6.10 Pointing

Use View/Point to read coordinates of the screen using the mouse.

10.6.11 Graphics setup

Persistent setup for graphics is set through the Graphics setup dialog.

10.7 Copy and paste

There is a distinction between use of the clipboard inside GiveWin, and that for external use.

When no area is selected, the whole graphics window is copied to the clipboard in WMF format, from which it can be pasted into other programs (either in WMF or in bitmap format). In addition, the graph is copied on the clipboard in a GiveWin-specific format.

When an area is selected, it is only copied to the clipboard in the GiveWin format.

When a GiveWin graphics format is on the clipboard, it can be added to an existing graph (no area selected) or to an existing area (which must be selected). Copying in the internal format is delayed, which means that the full copying is not actually performed until a paste is requested. This implies that when a graphics window is closed it is not available for pasting anymore.

It is not possible to paste from other programs into GiveWin graphs.

10.8 Working view

The Working View controls the size of the paper on screen. The default is 100, but if your computer runs in a low resolution, you could set this to 80 for example (note that the window does not automatically change size). Use Make default to keep this size between runs of GiveWin.

10.9 Graphs and sample selection

Apart from the correlogram and spectrum, all types of graphics will use all valid observations, just skipping over missing values.

The correlogram and spectrum use data starting from the first valid observation in the sample, and stopping at the first missing value thereafter.

Chapter 11

GiveWin data management

11.1 Creating data

File/New allows for the creation of a new database. All variables in a database have the same frequency. A sample period is required, but can be extended later.

11.2 Database font

View/Set Font will be especially useful to select a smaller or larger font size for displaying the database on screen. The selected font will also be used for printing and text windows.

11.3 Database description

A database can have a description for documentation purposes, and separate from the variable description. Only .IN7/.BN7 data files can preserve the description.

11.4 Printing data

Use File/Print when a database has the focus to print the database. The Database selection dialog which pops up allows printing of a subset of the database. File/Print Preview is available to view the result before printing.

The following control of headers and footers is available for printing from Tools/Page Setup:

- Draw a box around the graph;
- Draw a header for the graph. This is controlled via the Header and Footer boxes. There are four specials:
  - &[date] prints the date,
  - &[time] prints the time,

- &[page] prints the page number,
- &[file] prints the file name.

Other text in the edit field is printed directly.

To print more data on a page, the font size can be reduced, see the previous section.

11.5 Data formats

Data file formats are discussed in §8.1–§8.5.

11.6 Saving data

Use File/Save As or the diskette toolbar button to save the data to a disk file. At the bottom of the dialog is a dropdown listbox in which you select the type of file. When saving, a dialog will appear to allow the selection of a subset and subsample for saving.

11.7 Navigation and editing

A database cursor indicates which is the current observation. The cursor can be moved from the keyboard or using the mouse. A block of observations can be selected (highlighted) for:

- copying to the clipboard;
- as a destination for a block from the clipboard;
- to set to a single value: press Enter to specify the value, whence you will be prompted whether the value should be applied to the whole selection.

Press Enter or double click on an observation to edit the value. Algebra and the calculator allows manipulation of variables through mathematical expressions.

11.8 Renaming variables

Press Enter or double click on the variable name in the database to change the name or documentation. When in the Calculator, press Ins when a variable is selected in the list box to rename.

11.9 Deleting variables

Click on the variable name in the database to select the variable (or a group of variables), then press the Del key to delete (confirmation of the deletion will be required). When in the Calculator, press Del when a variable is selected in the list box to delete, confirmation will be required again.

11.10 Reordering variables

The variables listbox in the Calculator allows variables to be picked up with the mouse and moved down or up in the listbox.

11.11 Adding variables

Double click on an empty field in the database next to an existing variable to create a new variable. Alternatively use Edit/New Variable.

11.12 Extending the sample period

Double click on an empty field in the database below an existing variable to activate the Extend Database sample dialog. Alternatively use Edit/Extend sample.

11.13 Copy and paste

The standard copy and paste facilities are available, also see §11.7.

References

Davidson, J. E. H., Hendry, D. F., Srba, F. and Yeo, S. (1978). Econometric modelling of the ag-
gregate time-series relationship between consumers' expenditure and income in the United
Kingdom, *Economic Journal*, **88**, 661–692. Reprinted in Hendry D. F. (1993), *Economet-
rics: Alchemy or Science?* Oxford: Blackwell Publishers.

Granger, C. W. J. (1966). The typical spectral shape of an economic variable, *Econometrica*, **34**,
150–161.

Granger, C. W. J. and Newbold, P. (1986). *Forecasting Economic Time Series* 2nd edition. New
York: Academic Press.

Green, P. J. and Silverman, B. W. (1994). *Nonparametric Regression and Generalized Linear
Models. A Roughness Penalty Approach.* London: Chapman and Hall.

Härdle, W. (1990). *Applied Nonparametric Regression.* Cambridge: Cambridge University Press.

Harvey, A. C. (1993). *Time Series Models* 2nd edition. Hemel Hempstead: Harvester Wheatsheaf.

Hastie, T. J. and Tibshirani, R. J. (1994). *Generalized Additive Models.* London: Chapman and
Hall.

Koopman, S. J., Harvey, A. C., Doornik, J. A. and Shephard, N. (1995). *STAMP 5.0. Structural
Time Series Analyser Modeller and Predictor.* London: Chapman and Hall.

Priestley, M. B. (1981). *Spectral Analysis and Time Series.* London: Academic Press.

Ripley, B. D. (1987). *Stochastic Simulation.* New York: John Wiley & Sons.

Silverman, B. W. (1986). *Density Estimation for Statistics and Data Analysis.* London: Chapman
and Hall.

Subject Index

119